CW00556738

The Tram Driver

The Art of Tram Driving
revealed by David Tudor

Published by Adam Gordon

Cover Photographs
Photos by Glyn Wilton, Curator of the National Tramway Museum, Derbyshire.
Other photographs in this book are by the author unless otherwise credited.

ISBN 1-874422-65-6 (978-1-874422-65-5)
Publication no. 69
Published in 2006 by Adam Gordon, Kintradwell Farm, Brora, Sutherland KW9 6LU
Tel: 01408 622660
E-mail: adam@ahg-books.com

First printing limited to 500 copies

Printed by: Launton Digital Press Ltd, Oxfordshire
Production by: Trevor Preece, 2 Sella Bank, The Banks, Seascale, Cumbria CA20 1QU
E-mail: trevor@epic.gb.com

CONTENTS

PREFACE

Based on my experience gained over four decades of driving electric trams, and twenty years spent teaching others how to do so, I have been encouraged by friends to put on record all the best practices I have been taught and have observed concerning tram driving.

My working career began as an apprentice at the English Electric Company's Preston works, building and testing electrical control equipment and traction motors for railways. At the age of twenty-one I was promoted to Aircraft Inspector (Electrical) and transferred to the firm's Aircraft Division. Four years later a wish to learn German and a desire to get back into electric traction work took me to Cologne, where I was recruited by the city's Transport Company. Two years after my employment began in the tramway division I gained promotion to the post of Electrical Technician, and in that same year (early in 1968) was fortunate to spend three months in the tramway Driving School of the Kölner Verkehrs Betriebe (Cologne Transport). This was a full-time 38 hours-per-week course and included two days of theory and practical tests.

During this time my employers were about to commission their first section of underground tramway. I had the pleasure of driving the second passenger car ever to enter the subway during testing, almost a year before public service began. Although the modern Düwag articulated trams had taken over many routes in Cologne, eighty of its older cars relied on the hand-brake being used to hold the car (and trailer) at stops. There were also about twenty works cars whose control equipment was venerable (some had controllers with segments and fingers), and used the hand-brake to hold the car. Full training was given on these, and on the state of the art subway signalling. My time in the driving school spanned both traditional tramway practice and the new technology of light rail.

In this book I have used the term "heritage tramcar" to describe trams of a certain age and vintage. Not all heritage trams live in museums and some operators might be insulted if the description "museum tram" was applied to their working fleet! This book includes both recollections of my experiences and the shared knowledge of others with whom I have been privileged to discuss operating practices. It is not designed for use as a training manual, but is offered as a description of all that has been assimilated as good and robust working standards; methods which over many years have proven themselves to be both safe and reliable. The book has evolved from the training booklets written by me for use at the Garden Festival tramways at Gateshead and Glasgow, as well as at the National Tramway Museum, where I was for many years the Chief Driving Instructor. In 1998 I produced the training booklets and delivered the driver familiarisation courses for Blackpool Transport's select group of drivers, who had been chosen to drive two heritage tramcars at the resort, that had been loaned to the operator from Crich for the Fleetwood Tramroad Centenary celebrations.

Whilst this book is offered as a compendium of good practice, it should not be regarded as a "one-size-fits-all" solution to operating a tramway. Each tramway system will have its own features, most tramcar designs differ widely from each other; therefore, there can be no alternative to individual risk assessments, assessments of personal competence, and a training plan tailored to suit. Reference to current Health and Safety Legislation must be undertaken before producing any training information or plan.

David Tudor
Nottingham
November 2006

ACKNOWLEDGEMENTS

My grateful thanks go to all those friends who have assisted in the compilation of this book, especially with the loan of many photographs and drawings. I am grateful too for the kind permission to publish these items, and for the various items of information supplied. Special thanks go to John Shawcross, for supplying most of the drawings and for his editorial assistance; to Glyn Wilton – Curator of the National Tramway Museum; to Neil Jones of the Great Orme Tramway; Clive Pennington of Nottingham Express Transit; to Stan Grundy, John Henderson, and Thorsten Kurzawa of Berlin Transport.

Dedication

To the unsung heroes of the tramway industry – the driving instructors – whose fine example, patience, and singular determination enabled generations of trainees to become safe and competent drivers of a unique type of public service vehicle. Drivers whose job was demanding, sometimes standing for eight hours a day at the controls, and yet for most passengers remaining a distant shadow beyond the bulkhead doors.

CHAPTER 1

Basic Principles

Whilst this book is primarily concerned with electric tramcars, recognition must be made of the other forms of traction: horse, steam, and cable. The National Tramway Museum began its public operation using a horse-powered tram before the start of an electric tramway service, and this was a fruitful form of learning. Among the things we learnt was that some horses were positively destructive towards even a small tram. Another was the need for two persons to be on the front platform: a tram driver, and an experienced equine handler. One other dilemma is still unresolved: is it preferable in the case of a horse that becomes distressed to release its harness from the tram's coupling, or to keep it coupled up? This should be the focus of any organisation's Risk Assessment study if horse operation is planned.

Limited operation of the steam tram engine "John Bull" at Crich gave me the opportunity of driving such a vehicle, and finally proved for me the superiority of electric traction. A suitable steam tram trailer exists in the Crich Collection in the form of Dundee 21, but the fitting of some form of continuous braking is essential before the demonstration of a steam powered tram-train can be carried out.

Cable trams are always associated with San Francisco. Edinburgh once had an extensive system of cable trams, now long gone. The Great Orme Tramway in Llandudno survives and flourishes under its new management. Unlike San Francisco where the cable trams use a jaw-like gripper to grab the endless cable, the Welsh variety is permanently attached to the haulage cable. Subjected to the scrutiny of H.M. Railway Inspectorate, the refurbishment of the entire infrastructure in 2001-2 was followed by the training of the operating staff in accordance with current standards. Operating procedures had to be submitted, these being formulated and compiled with the assistance of the author.

1.1 Safety First

Always keep these inherent dangers in mind when in charge of a tram:

- First and foremost, like any form of machinery, trams can kill and seriously injure people if not operated correctly and accidents occur.
- Secondly, a tram is a heavy form of vehicle that once out of control presents a serious life-threatening hazard.
- Thirdly, most trams use electricity at more than double the voltage of a domestic supply, so a tramcar combines the dangerous features of machinery, and a large and heavy vehicle, with those of an electricity sub-station.

A tram driver not only has to know how to drive the vehicle, but what to do in an emergency or abnormal situation. He/she must safeguard and promote the safety of passengers, as well as that of other road users, and secure the preservation of evidence after an accident. The driver is the staff member who in the absence of more senior staff must take charge if a crisis occurs. It is important that he/she wears a full uniform (including cap, sturdy footwear, and – if on the public highway – high visibility clothing). Never attempt to drive a heritage tram while wearing sandals or soft footwear – the handbrake ratchet may cause injury to your foot. Drivers who require spectacles for ordinary vision should not drive open-fronted trams in the rain.

Being smartly turned out will support the authority of the driver, as will an attitude of professional competence. In an age where security issues are paramount the tram's crew must monitor passengers, and what they may attempt to bring on board the tram. On a heritage tramway it may be awkward baby-buggies, while passengers on public service modern trams may need dissuading from bringing gas-bottles, sharp-edged tools etc, on to busy vehicles. Drivers must know and apply the regulations that concern the transport of animals.

1.2 Taking Care

Recent changes to legislation have introduced the principle of a duty of care. This means that while driving a tram (as well as in countless other human activities) the driver has a duty of care towards anyone who may be affected while those driving activities are being carried out. Failure to apply this principle may result in legal proceedings being instigated – especially where safety standards appear to have been ignored. Members of staff need to constantly ponder the question: have I, in carrying out my duties, taken all reasonably practical precautions? Exercising care for others includes those persons who are neglectful of their own safety (e.g. "surfers" and anyone attempting to board or alight from a moving tram).

When driving a tram which is also part of a museum collection, a second duty of care must be respected – that of a specific curatorial responsibility. This means not subjecting the tram to any excessive speed, acceleration, or braking (except in an emergency). The word "curator" means someone who takes care of an object, and this must be the guiding principle of anyone demonstrating (i.e. not "driving" in the everyday sense of the word) an exhibit that is part of a museum collection.

1.3 What Trams Can and Cannot Do

As most children soon learn, trams are steered by the rails upon which they run. This has both advantages and disadvantages. First, unlike a lorry driver, the tram-driver does not have to constantly keep the vehicle steered in the correct lane. However, being always guided by the track, the tram-driver cannot steer the tram away from danger (or obstructions) within the "swept path" of the tramway. This rules out the most frequently used accident avoidance technique of other road users – swerving out of harm's way. The tram-driver must therefore be capable of stopping the tram in the shortest possible distance at all times and in all weather conditions. Use of audible warnings can alert pedestrians who may be intent on emerging behind other trams or parked vehicles. A defensive driving attitude is essential for all tram-drivers, as is the talent for making a swift but accurate judgement of clearances and widths.

Vigilance while driving is essential, especially on street tramways. Whenever danger lurks the tram's speed must be reduced so that if needed an emergency stop can be made in the shortest possible distance and so avoid injury to other road users.

Adhesion is the word used to describe the grip of the tram's steel wheels on the steel tramlines. When adhesion is poor the tram wheels will either slip or slide. When the wheels slip they spin, and when they slide they cease to rotate – the skid involving two steel surfaces means that the effect is to turn the tram into a sledge!

The coefficient of adhesion, ie, the limit beyond which the grip of the wheels on the rails cannot be relied upon; this especially when starting, between wheel and rail can vary, see the table here:

Table 1

Rail condition	Coefficient of adhesion
Dry rail	0.25
Thoroughly wet rail	0.18 to 0.2
Moist or greasy rail	0.15
When sand is applied	0.25 to 0.3

It should be noted that the coefficient of adhesion reduces with an increase of speed.

Sand applied between the wheels and rail (and a temporary reduction of power or braking) can correct the slip or slide of the tram. When adhesion is poor (i.e. damp rails and leaves on the line) use of the tram's sanding equipment is essential. Yes, it is true about the wrong kind of leaves being especially troublesome – an early autumnal frost brings down leaves still full of sap. When they get crushed on the rail surface the sap adheres to the railhead like a film of soap. A fully wet rail is almost as good as a dry one, but beware when it starts to rain following a long dry spell. A good tram-driver will soon learn to recognise the "mackerel" warning pattern of the dangerously slippery rail surface.

Differential gears – used on automobiles for many years – allow the two wheels on each end of the driving axle to rotate at differing speeds, and therefore provide an important feature assisting cornering. Heritage tramcars do not have this facility, and while negotiating curves one wheel on each axle will (indeed, must) slip or slide. This handicap prevents effective braking on curves, as does also the sideways displacement of the sand pipes causing sand not to fall on the rail top. The remedy is always to traverse curves at a very low speed.

1.4 The Effect of Weight

The effect of laden weight (i.e. passengers) can surprise the unwary. Drivers of large goods lorries will tell you of the difference between driving a heavily laden lorry and an automobile. Whilst the motorist will feel the car slow down as soon as the brake-pedal is depressed, the lorry driver will warn of a much slower response when braking because of the much heavier weight involved. First generation trams weigh between eight and eighteen tonnes and can convey up to four tonnes of passengers. Even on excellent rail conditions with good adhesion new drivers will often be surprised (especially on falling gradients) how long it takes to stop. Indeed, if the wheels skid, so little braking effect is generated that the braking effect is reduced to one tenth of the normal braking performance. This means that instead of stopping the tram in ten metres it will take one hundred metres to do so. An uncorrected skid will also wear a "flat" on any wheel involved in the slide – a defect that may cause the tram's withdrawal from service for remedial action in the workshop.

When towing either a trailer or a disabled tram, beware of the extra weight, especially in the case of a failed power car without full braking capability. You may find that when braking, the extra load will push your car.

There are three distinct stages within the braking event:

- The thinking distance.
- The response distance.
- The braking application.

The thinking distance involves the metres that the tram covers during the thought processes of the driver (Do I need to put the brakes on? Yes I do, are my hands in the right position? They always should be!).

The response distance is the ground covered during which time the brake handle is being moved and the mechanical linkage swings into action to commence the braking application.

Basic physics determine the braking application, and apart from the driver perfecting his braking skills and using sand properly, there is little scope for improvement. Likewise the response distance is a mechanical event with little room for improvement. However, the human factor behind the thinking distance is where the greatest scope for improvement lies. It can be shortened by the driver both developing a good sense of anticipation (swiftly identifying a potentially dangerous situation), as well as developing a lightning-quick response enabling valuable seconds

Table 2

Stopping Distance

Speed	Thinking	Braking	Brake Application	Total
30km/h	6m	2m	4m	12m total
45km/h	9m	3m	11m	23m total
60km/h	12m	4m	20m	36m total

(equalling overall braking distance) to be gained. As stated elsewhere, having one's hands in the right places helps the driver save valuable time and shortens the braking distance.

The figures quoted in Table 2 are based on a thinking time of just under a second; an alert and experienced driver can reduce this to a half-second.

1.5 What You Cannot Do

You cannot drive a tram after consuming alcohol, or if under prescribed medication which could affect your performance, or while under the influence of drugs. Under the Transport and Works Act 1992 anyone involved in any safety critical work on a transport system who ignores these regulations can be prosecuted and may lead to a criminal conviction, fine or imprisonment.

It is imperative that any candidate to be trained as a driver must be able to read and write. As part of the medical examination, the candidate will be tested for physical stamina and good reaction times (e.g. hitting a pedal or button when a red light appears or a warning buzzer is sounded).

A benchmark of competence means that anyone who drives a tram must have been trained and assessed (supported by documentary evidence) and have the authority to carry out such duties. Regulations are coming into force limiting tram drivers' hours, to prevent tiredness or fatigue impairing their driving skills.

Steam trams were not the cleanest of vehicles, as this photo of a depot facility shows. This shot is a mystery – it was sent to me by a German friend, but without any details of the location. Could it be the Chiemseebahn in Bavaria? ***Photographer Unknown***

Government legislation requires all drivers of tram or light rail vehicles to be in possession of a valid Road Driving Licence, issued by the DVLA of class B or higher. No one whose DVLA licence is subject to disqualification or suspension may drive a tram.

How it all started in most cities. The horse drawn tram is followed by the electric cars. Animal traction was highly expensive. Four times as many horses were needed as trams, and the animals had to be fed and looked after even when they were not able to work. Not only were veterinary fees a large element in the operating costs, but also horse manure was a serious health hazard in the larger cities. This Cologne horse car 211 photographed during the 125 years jubilee celebrations in 2002 survived for many years as a trailer hauled by its electric successors.

CHAPTER 2

Practical Knowledge

2.1 Basic Electrical Theory

To understand the basic principles of electric propulsion as applied to tramcars, it is first necessary to consider a little basic physics. Electric current flows in circuits, and always returns to where it starts its course. In the nineteenth century many people thought of electricity as a fluid, and it is easy to compare its behaviour with water – although one should never mix the two things in practice!

Voltage is the scale by which we measure electrical tension, rather like the head of water held back by a high dam, or the pressure at which water is held in a hose-pipe with the tap at the end closed.

Amperes (or Amps for short) is the unit of measurement for the flow of current around a circuit. The 'resistance' value of an electrical circuit (or of components in that circuit) affects the amount of current able to flow in an inverse proportion.

In plain English, if the voltage present remains constant, a higher current will flow when the resistance is reduced, and (vice versa), increasing the amount of resistance will reduce the current able to flow.

The general basic circuit of an electric tramway using an overhead line supply and a rail-based (earth) return current path is shown in Diagram 2.

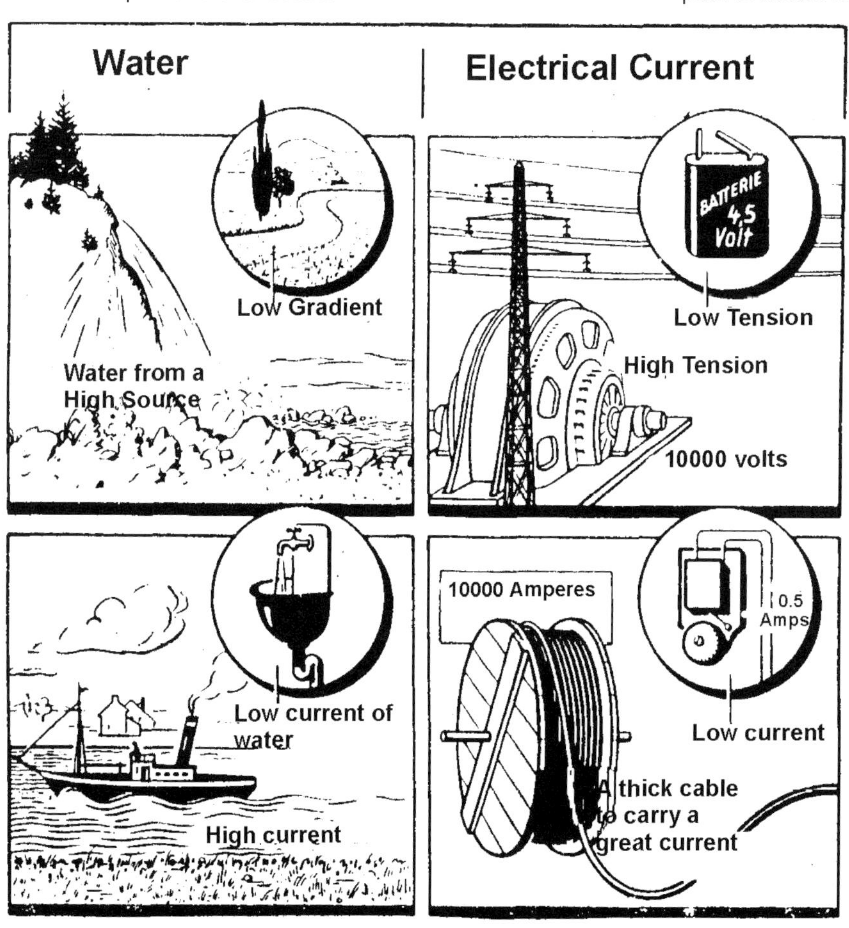

Diagram 1
Comparisons are made in these four windows – the round inset window shows the opposite of the main picture in terms of pressure (top), and the flow of current – the lower two examples.

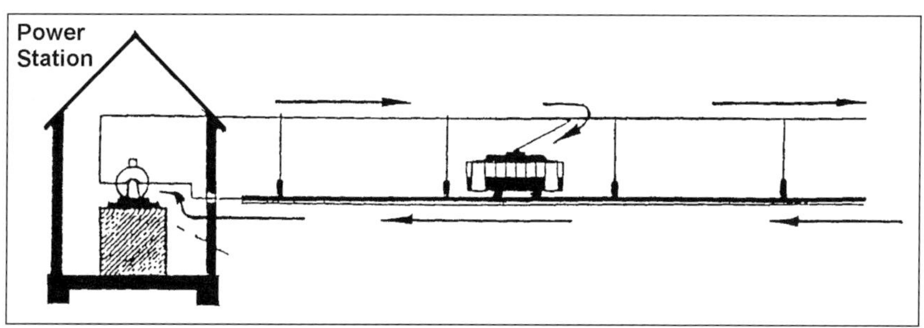

Diagram 2

2.2 Electricity and the Tramcar

Electricity is generated at a power station. It is conveyed at a very high voltage through the national grid distribution system. The typical traction sub-station receives its supply at 11,000 volts and is three-phase alternating current. After being transformed and rectified, the electrical supply fed to the tramway overhead line is a nominal 600 volts* and is direct current (or DC for short). Special equipment in the sub-station protects against overloading, peak-voltage surges, and earth faults.

The positive line feed to each tramcar is taken from the overhead line by means of the current-collector – this can be a trolley-pole, a pantograph, or a bow-collector.

The negative line conveying the return current from the tramcar's wheels is connected to the tramway rails.

Conduit tramway construction usually had a twin set of conductor rails buried within the conduit – one positive and one negative. The "Plough" was built with two current collecting shoes: one positive, and the other being of negative polarity. There were other forms of current supply devised to overcome the widespread objection to overhead wires.

Surface contact systems became extinct in England not long after the First World War. These consisted of studs set about six feet apart in the centre line between tram rails. When a tram passed over them a magnetic field

* Britain's new tramways use the slightly higher 750-volt supply, following the trend set by new tramways in other countries.

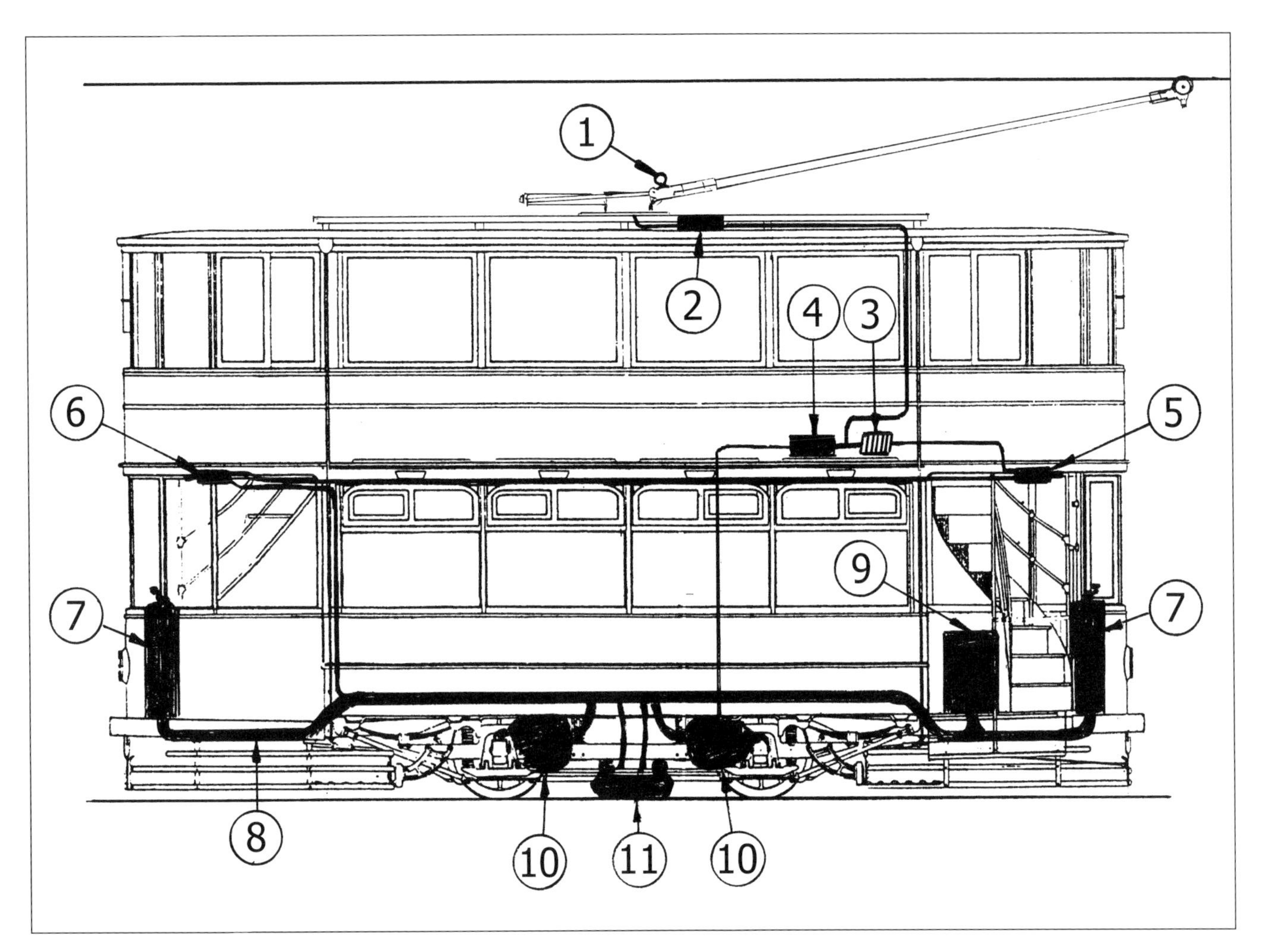

Diagram 3
Main components in the traction system

1 Trolley cable
2 Main fuse
3 Lightning arrestor
4 Choke coil
5 Circuit breaker number 1
6 Circuit breaker number 2
7 Controller
8 Traction wiring looms
9 Resistors (platform mounted)
10 Traction motor
11 Magnetic track brake

closed a switch inside the stud housing. This made the stud live and fed power into a long skate mounted under the tram. After the tram had passed beyond the reach of the stud, another was ready to take its place. The main weakness was a reluctance of the contact studs to de-energise after the tram had gone. An earthing brush was fitted to the rear fender of each tram to disarm rogue studs.

A modern variation has recently emerged in France. The new tramway in Bordeaux has been partly equipped with a system known as SOL. In this a "third rail" variant of the old studs is divided into 10-metre long sections. The passage of the articulated trams causes each section to be energised in turn, and de-energised when the tram leaves the section. Various teething problems have been reported.

How a traditional current supply gets to the tram. (Numbers refer to drawing above) The tram's main supply cable begins at the current collector – in the case of a trolley pole, the cable usually running inside the hollow centre of the boom (1). The first item connected to the incoming supply is the main fuse (2) (This is a modern safety feature). Next follow the lightning-arrestor (3) along with its associated choke coil (4). The purpose of these two is explained by diagram 5 on page 12. The electrical circuit continues from the choke coil (at which place a branch circuit diverges and feeds the auxiliary equipment e.g. lighting) to the first of two main (traction) circuit-breakers (5) and (6). These are connected following the most common practice in a series connection, so current flows first through one circuit-breaker, and then through the other. Therefore, both circuit-breakers have to be switched "on" before current can reach the controllers (7). A hundred years ago it was thought that one automatic circuit breaker was sufficient per tram. A canopy switch was fitted at one end of the car – although similar in appearance to a circuit breaker it was simply an on/off switch. The main circuit-breakers act as an overload protection and will trip out if a pre-set level of current is exceeded – this is the equivalent of blowing a fuse in a domestic installation. The most frequent cause of overload is an excessive rate of acceleration – this is usually a product of inappropriate driving techniques! With both circuit-breakers being connected in series, it is not unusual for the unit on the back platform to trip. Although this feature may seem inconvenient, it does mean from that in an emergency the conductor can stop the tram from the rear platform (by tripping the circuit-breaker at his/her end, and then applying the hand-brake). A few operators did connect their cars' Circuit-Breakers in Parallel. Whilst this removes the problem of the back-end breaker tripping out, it also rules out use of the emergency procedure described above.

If the full (line) voltage were connected to the traction motors (10) when they were stationary the result would be a massive overload. By first connecting the motors in a series connection (one after the other) and also introducing resistance grids (resistors) (9) into the circuit the current flowing through the traction motors is limited and the motors increase in speed only gradually. Once the tram and its motors gather speed, the resistance can be lowered by moving the controller main handle to a further notch – this means that a higher speed will be attained. At the final notch in the Series portion of the notches no resistance is connected and each motor receives a half of the line voltage i.e. 600V ÷ 2 = 300V. This is the most economic running notch.

Moving the main handle further in a clockwise direction passes through a transition section which reconnects the traction motors in a parallel configuration – i.e. the motors now receive the full line voltage. Once again it is necessary to introduce resistance into the circuit to limit the current, until advancing the main handle through the notches the final parallel notch is reached, and the tram will attain its full speed. The other notches (at the opposite side of the off position) connect the motors into a braking mode, and are described later.

It is important to remember that the traction motors are connected directly by gearing to the driving axles; there is no clutch as on a lorry or bus. Reversing direction is achieved by altering the electrical polarity of the traction motor armatures by moving the controller key to "reverse" – only to be done when the tram is stationary.

Tramcar resistors (9), like an electric fire, convert electrical energy into heat, and can overheat if used for an excessive time. It is possible that over-heating may cause a fire. Drivers should never dwell on resistance notches for more than 20 seconds, but progress as rapidly as passenger comfort permits to either full series or full parallel. It is bad practice to move the main controller handle beyond full series if the possibility of reaching full parallel is unrealistic.

Electric braking is frequently called rheostatic braking (or in railway parlance: dynamic braking) and these terms more accurately describe how electric braking is achieved on most heritage trams. Rheostatic braking uses the tram's motors acting as generators, and they retard the tram once an electrical load in the form of the car's resistance grids (rheostats) is connected across the output of the motors. Reducing the amount of resistance increases the load, until when the final brake notch is selected, there is an effective short circuit across the terminals. Put into other words: the rheostatic brake converts the moving tram's mechanical (or kinetic) energy into electrical energy; this is then converted into heat by the resistors.

Regenerative braking is described in section 3. Magnetic track brakes (11) can be fitted, and being fed from the braking circuit will exert extra braking force proportional to the strength of the braking current being generated. Certain operators used magnetic track brakes fed from the 600-volt supply. Not only did these units tend to overheat if left switched on, but any interruption in the traction supply led to failure of the track brakes.

Once the tram's traction motors no longer rotate fast enough to generate current, the braking effect diminishes and this results in the tramcar being brought not quite to a stop. So, at speeds under 5mph there is insufficient electrical output to stop the car, and mechanical braking must be applied at this low speed, as well as to hold the car stationary.

Most controller top plates are clearly marked: "Series", "Parallel", "Off" and "Brake". During the 1920s and later an air interlock box became a common feature mounted on top of tramcar controllers – the function of these will be described later.

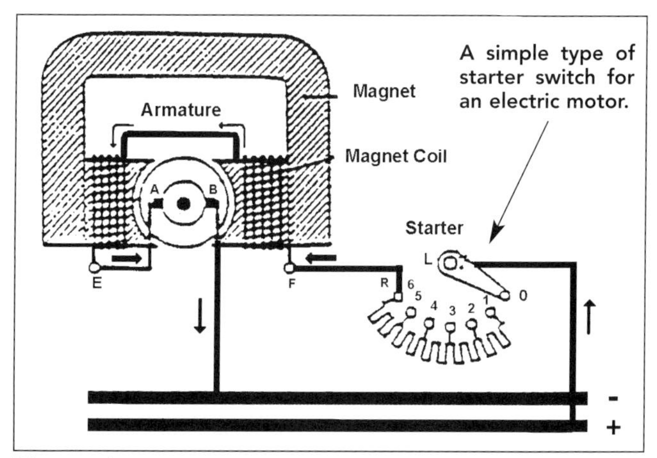

Diagram 4

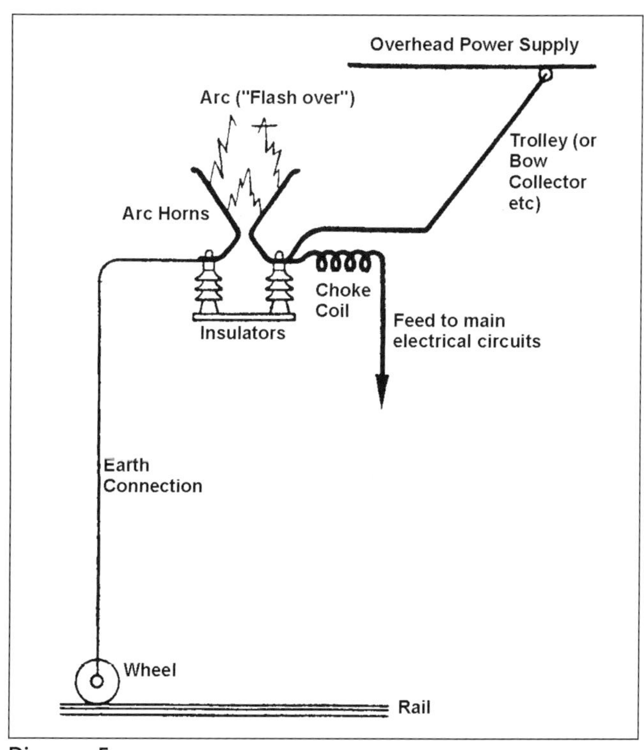

Diagram 5

The important components are the arrestor – here shown with two horns, but usually a more modern enclosed type is fitted – and the choke coil, which acts as a buffer to the excess voltage, causing such surges to be deflected into the arrestor where it is "flashed-over" back to earth.

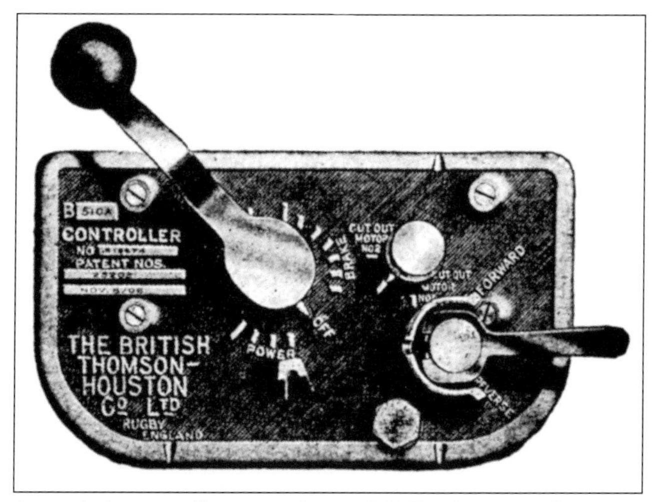

A typical controller top (type B510) showing the main power/brake handle at the "Off" position. Clockwise can be seen the series notches, whilst at the other side of "Off" are the brake notches. The small (removable) handle on the right is the controller key, sometimes called the reverser key.

Overhead wires form a natural lightning conductor, and to prevent damage to the electrical equipment, lightning arrestors are connected to the supply equipment at the sub-station, at certain locations on the overhead line, as well as fitted to the tram as shown on the previous page.

The electrical current returns from the motors through the axles and steel chassis of the tram, then via the rails back to the supplying sub-station.

Earthing

The electrical safety of a tramcar is greatly enhanced by the bonding to the chassis of all metal components of the body-

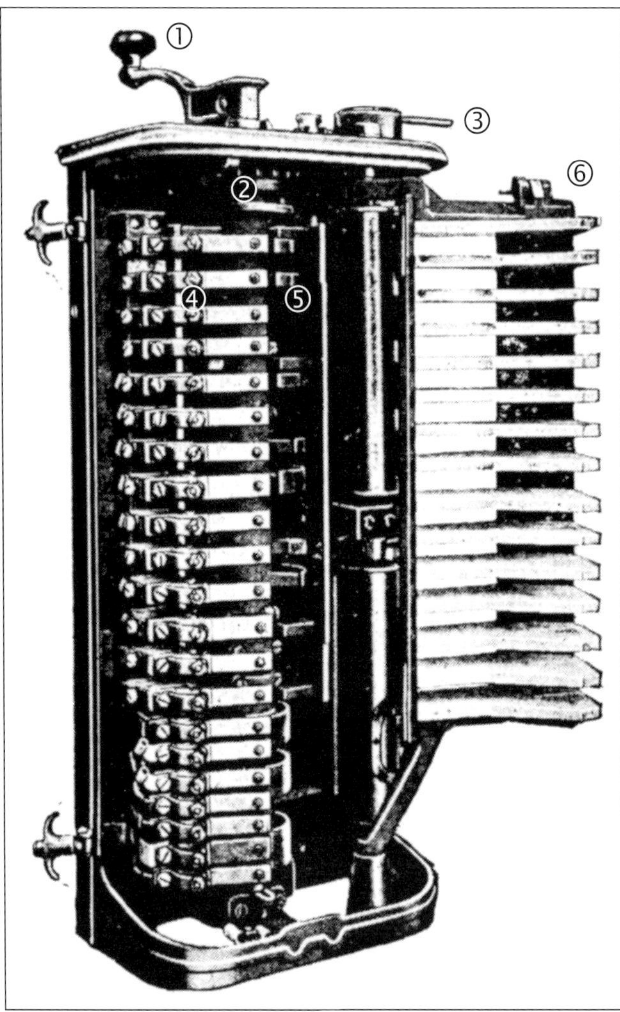

Schedule of Controller's Main Components.
1: Handle. 2: Barrel. 3: Key. 4: Fingers. 5: Segments. 6: Arc shutes.

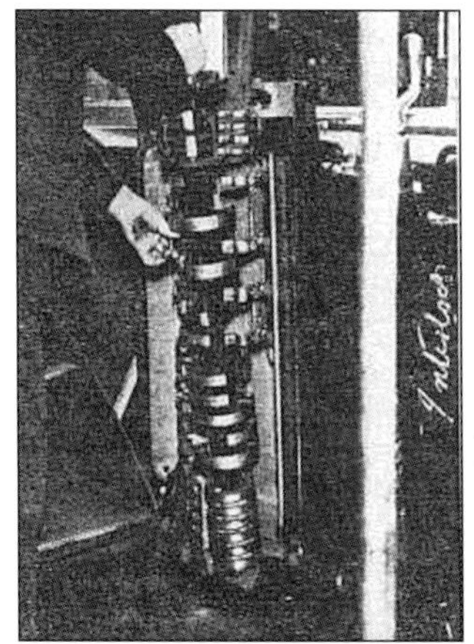

A Westinghouse T2C controller – this view showing the dismantling and removal of the barrel.

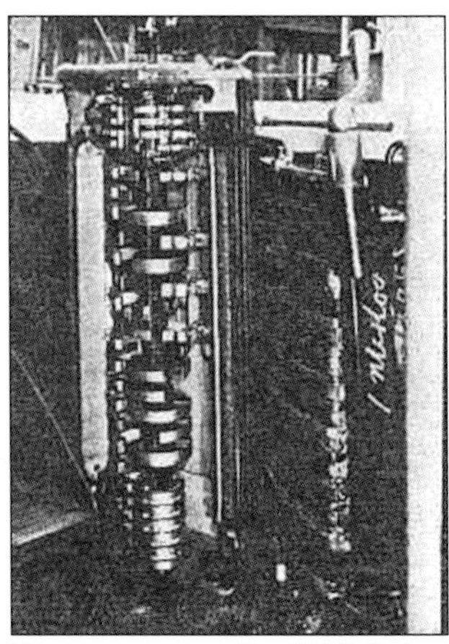

The same controller (T2C) being re-assembled. The arc shutes are swung clear showing the barrel quite clearly.

WARNING

The interior photographs of controllers on these pages are shown for general information only.

These items can cause electrocution if mishandled.

2.3 Diagrams 6a, 6b, 6c

A schematic diagram of a tramcar with four motors and modern contactor control gear.
F= field coils, R = resistor-contactor, LS = line switch, B = braking contactors, P, G, & S = grouping contactors.

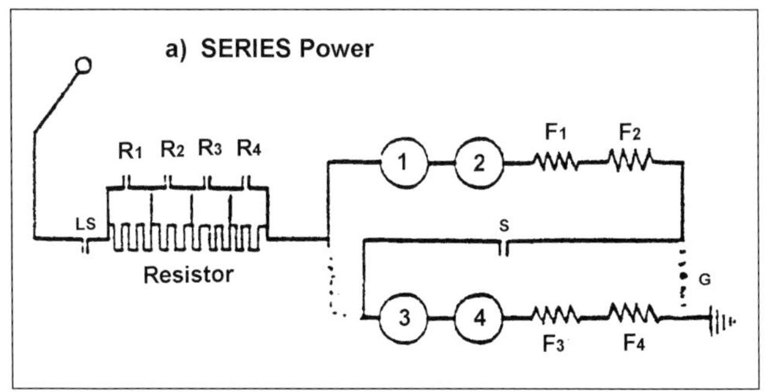

SERIES power: The broken lines in all three drawings represent connections that are not in use. The first notches close switches LS, then R1, R2, etc, bridging out sections of resistor grid until at the full series notch all are closed and no resistance is in circuit.

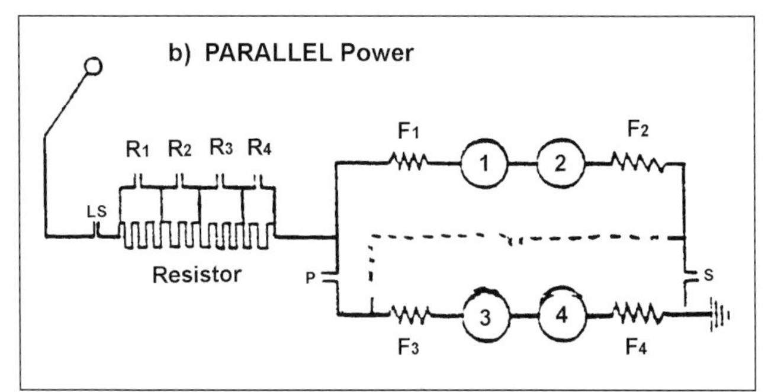

PARALLEL power: The process described above is repeated once the transition from series to (here) the parallel connection has been made. At the final notch all switches R1 to R4 etc, are closed.

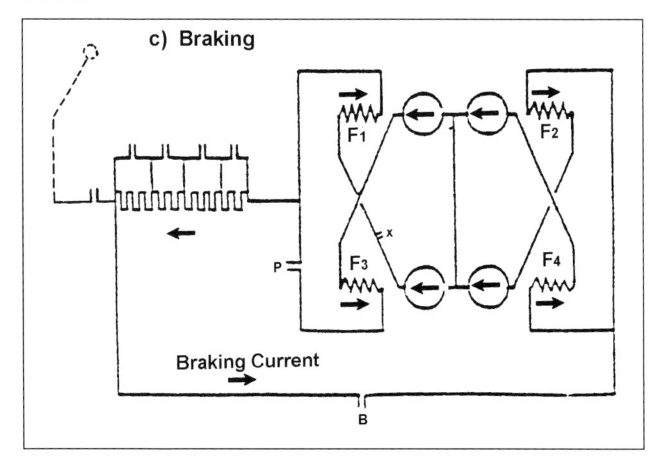

BRAKING: Once the electric braking mode has been selected the switches again close as the controller handle is moved. Once all are closed the current from the motors is effectively in a short-circuit. Note that the power supply is now redundant in this mode. Braking is totally self-contained, available even if the tram is derailed and devoid of traction power.

work and the metal casing of such things as controllers. This means that any failure of insulation results in a short-circuit to earth, and the swift operation of circuit breaker or fuse to cut off the supply.

Additionally, modern safety procedures prescribe that when equipment is being worked on, the electrical supply is not just switched off, but the tram's current collector is also bonded to earth by means of switches that can be locked in this position.

2.4 Brakes

Every tram must possess at least two independent forms of braking – in the case of heritage trams: a mechanical brake usually acting on the wheel tread (i.e. applied by hand, or possibly by air pressure), and an electric brake created by using the traction motors as generators. This electric rheostatic brake is most effective in bringing a tramcar to a near halt rapidly, but its effectiveness ceases below 5mph. It will not function when the tram is stationary, and so the hand-brake must always be used once the car has almost stopped.

Tramcars fitted with a compressed-air braking system typically apply friction-brakes to the wheels and/or to the track shoes or slippers. Brakes which operate on the rails are extremely effective even under bad rail conditions. They can be applied by mechanical effort – usually by turning a wheel concentric to the hand-brake handle, or by means of compressed air applied when the driver uses the emergency brake notches. London's tramways standardised on the solenoid track brake. This comprised a heavy electro-magnet suspended by springs just above the rail surface. Being in two parts, each having a north pole and a south pole polarised shoe, the rail became like the "keeper" placed across the two faces of a horseshoe magnet. Energised by braking current (or by an on-board battery on new generation trams), its ability to stop the tram became legendary.

Mechanically applied track-brakes were often wound on at the top of inclines, and the tram driven on power, causing it to slide downhill suitably retarded. Any additional braking was achieved by use of the normal service brake. This feature was a regular practice in Lisbon.

On heritage tramcars not fitted with air-brakes or fully engineered for service use of the electric brake, braking is by means of the mechanical hand-brake. The hand-cranked lever has ratchets both in the brass swan-neck handle, and at the foot of the brake-staff. By use of the two ratchets a very swift brake-application can be made, and the brake locked on. A typical four-wheel tramcar will have brake rigging employing chains, rods, and levers, as shown in diagram 7 below:

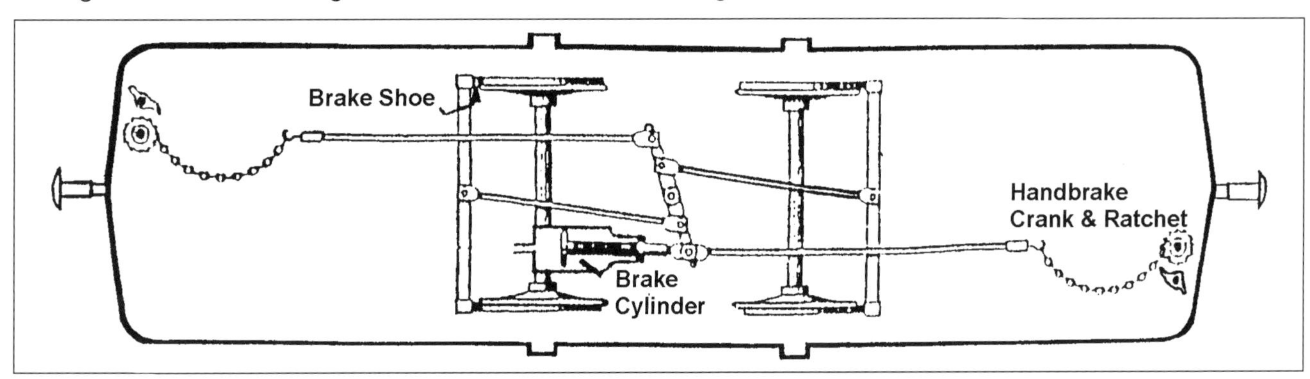

Diagram 7. A bird's eye view of a simple air/hand braking arrangement on a trailer tramcar.

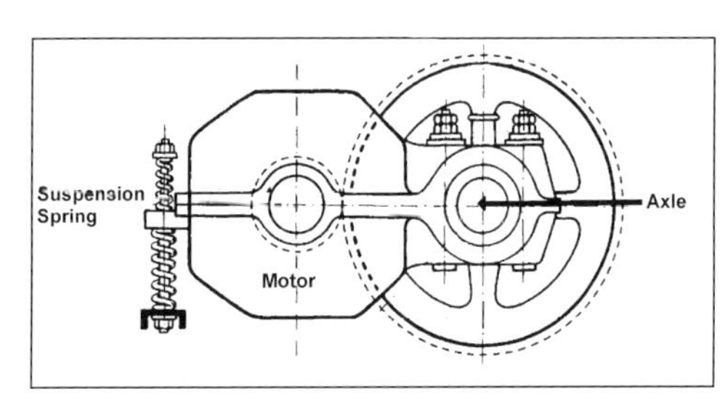

Diagram 8
Left: A cross-section through motor, gearing and axle.

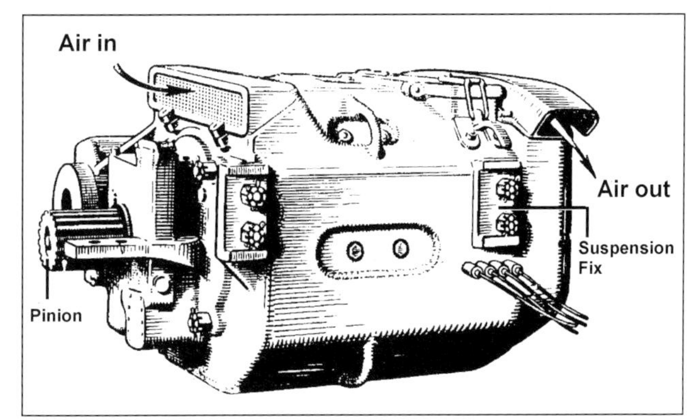

Diagram 9
A typical tramcar motor is of 25-70 horsepower.

2.5 Important Mechanical Details

As diagram 8 shows, a half of the weight of the motor rests unsprung on the driving axle supported by sleeve bearings. Any bumps or knocks affect the motor's brushes, these losing contact with the commutator. Such jolts can lead to electrical flash-overs – which is the term describing severe arcing resulting from the motor's carbon brushes losing contact. This is usually caused if power is applied when traversing such locations as points, crossings, and defective rail-joints. To lessen the danger of severely damaging motors, drivers should switch off power and coast through such track.

A simple gear and pinion transmits the mechanical power from the motor to the driving axle and wheels. The flanged wheels carry the weight of the tram and drive, and steer it! Both the tread and flange of tramcar wheels are less than one half the width and depth of equivalent dimensions for railway wheels and their flanges (see the diagram 24 on p.19). The wheel usually consists of a wheel centre (spoked or solid disc) surrounded by a steel tyre that is shrunk on to the wheel centre. Worn tyres can therefore be replaced without making a new wheel.

Interpoles became a feature of modern tramcar motors after World War I. As shown in diagram 10 they are quite thin and fitted between the main field-poles. Wired in series with the armature the interpoles change polarity when the motor is made to reverse its direction of rotation. It is acknowledged that they improve commutation (i.e. prevent sparking at the brushes). They do this by cutting off the magnetic influence of neighbouring main field coils – their own magnetic field is in opposition – just at the point corresponding with

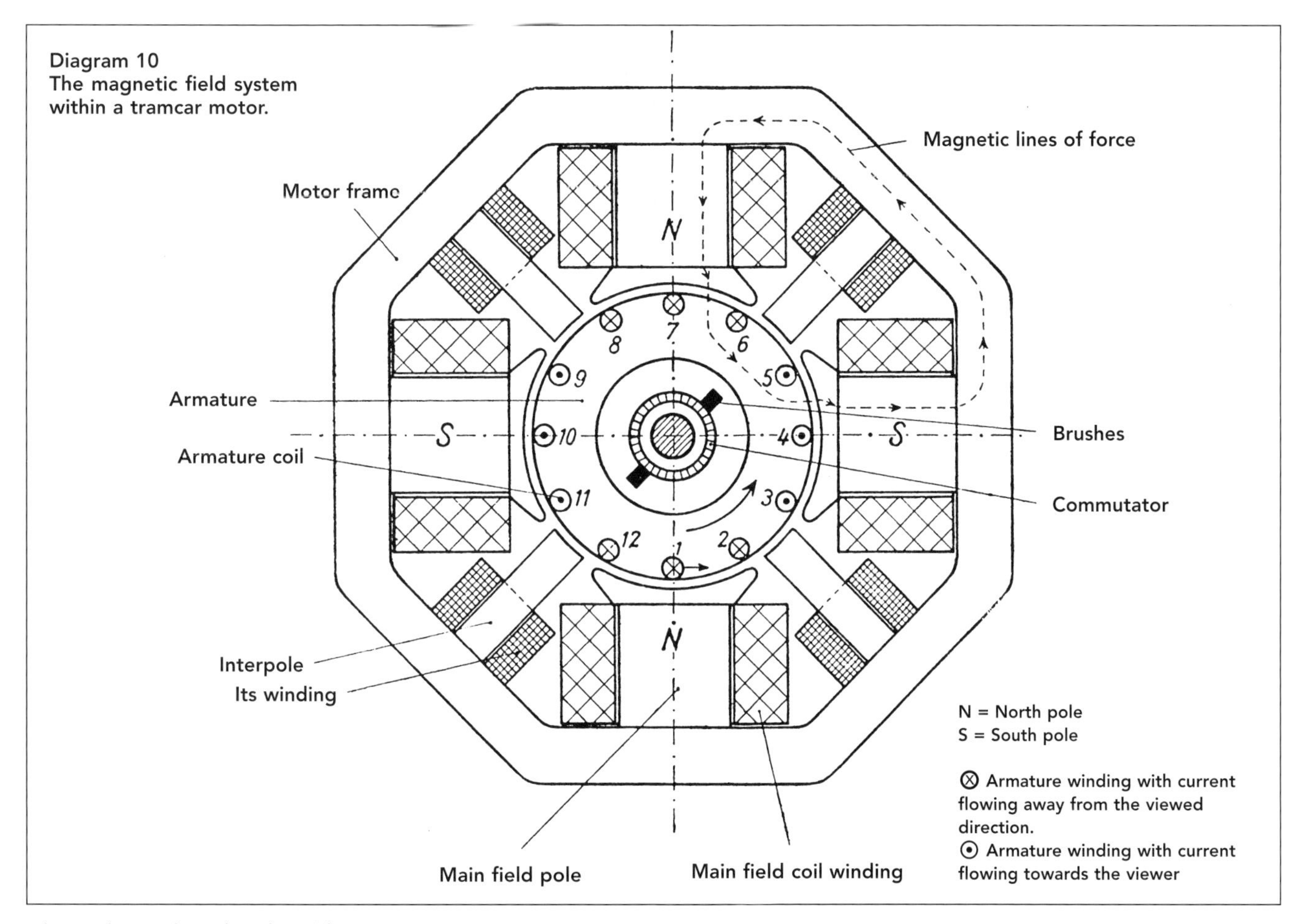

Diagram 10
The magnetic field system within a tramcar motor.

where the carbon brushes (that are wider than commutator bars) short out adjacent bars as the armature rotates.

The Driver's Best Friend

This is undoubtedly sand, and use of this can mean the difference between stopping the tram in the right place and having a collision!

In towns where trams are commonplace, police at an accident site involving a tram will measure the length of sand in the rail groove. This indicates the distance between the place where the driver first reacted and the location of the collision. Sand has to be stored in a dry place – many first-generation tramways had sand-drying plants at depots. Sand has to be of the correct type – not too fine and not too coarse – and certainly not dug from a beach with so much water and salt content that the sand hoppers corrode. One operator known to the author purchases the filtered-out sand from a glass foundry whose tankers deliver direct to the depots.

If the sand is to be carried outdoors from the depot storage place or bin, covered containers are essential. Filling the tramcar's hoppers should be done at the start of the driving duty and topped up as

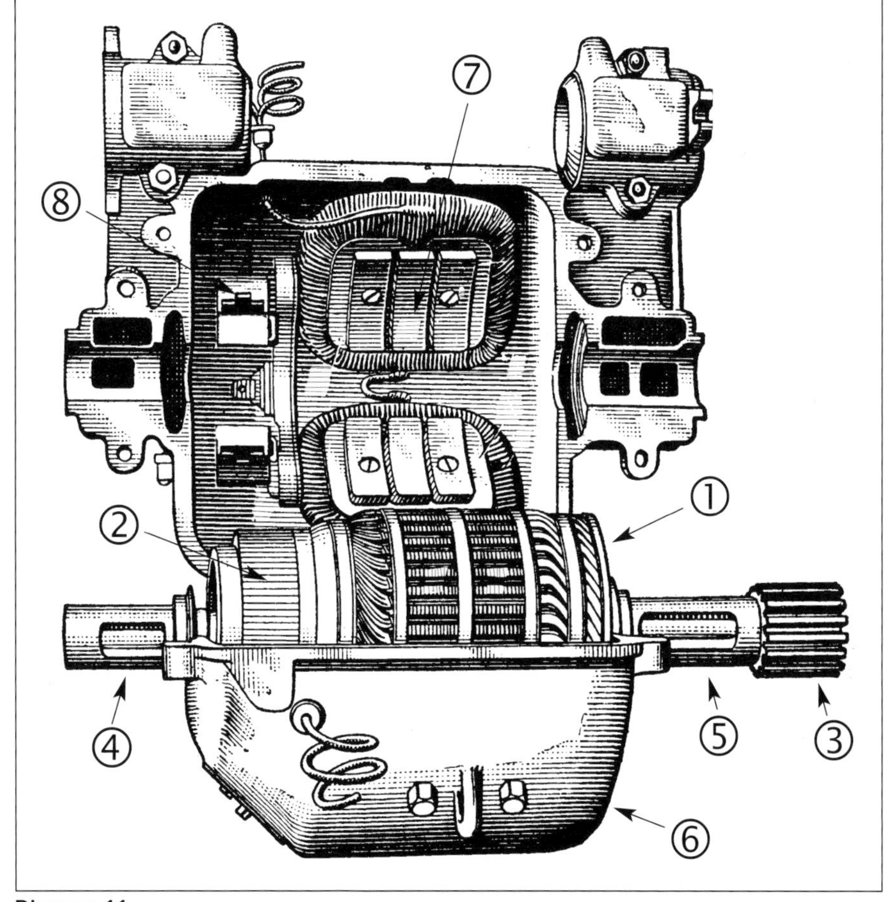

Diagram 11
Schedule of main components
1 Armature
2 Commutator
3 Pinion (gear)
4 Armature bearing
5 Armature bearing
6 Case
7 Field coil
8 Brush gear (carbon brushes and holders)

required during the operating day. The use of sand will be higher during autumn and whenever damp rails are encountered. Sand can be dropped on the rails (away from points and crossings) to aid adhesion during ordinary driving, in this case in conjunction with a reduction in acceleration by reducing power. Emergency application is best done by repeatedly depressing the sand pedal – this will ensure that sand continues to fall down the pipes, as the vibration of the valve opening and closing will keep the sand on the move. "Back sanders" is the name given to the facility fitted to trams operating hilly routes whereby sand was dropped behind the wheels – essential to enable the wheels of a tram slipping backwards to gain adhesion.

Certain tramcars were fitted with automatic sanding devices and/or sanders actuated by compressed air – sometimes operated by a trigger device mounted on the airbrake valve. The automatic sanders use either air (in which case a cam-actuated valve fitted to the interlock box comes into play), or a small solenoid – which in the event of severe rheostatic braking will pull on the mechanical linkage connected to the sand pedal and cause sand to be dropped. With modern technology it is possible to detect a wheel slip or slide within a second's delay. One of the earliest systems was the "Simatic" control system (Siemens 1968). This not only caused sand to drop, but intervened in the control system to reduce acceleration or braking – leaving the real driver with a feeling of "Who's really driving this tram!"

2.6 The Tramway and its Overhead Installation

An electric tramway is an electrical circuit with overhead trolley wires carrying 600 volts to each car drawing current from the overhead line. As seen already, the return path of the current is through the rails and track-bonds. Whilst tram-drivers quite properly pay good attention to the track, it is also important that drivers constantly observe the overhead-line equipment – i.e. not just the trolley wire, but also span wires, insulators, section-breakers, and frogs. This is important for two reasons – (1) the driver should switch off power and coast through section-breakers and frogs (please note: excessive arcing can only be prevented by applying this rule; furthermore, such arcing can damage the frog and lead to following cars' current collectors being severely damaged) and (2) vigilance is necessary so that the driver can identify any damaged overhead equipment, and bring the tram to a stop before the current collector reaches the damaged equipment. Only this will avoid causing even greater damage or a disaster such as falling overhead. Even the fourteen kilogrammes of upward pressure of a trolley pole can cause a short-circuit when a detached piece of wiring is forced into contact with components bonded to earth.

BEWARE of sub-station automatic equipment that will repeatedly attempt to re-energise the overhead line after any overload. Treat all items of overhead line equipment as **LIVE** and any part of overhead line equipment (even that lying on the ground) as potentially **LETHAL**. Remember too, that the overhead wiring is also under considerable mechanical tension, and this alone can seriously injure anyone interfering with it!
BE SAFE – STAY WELL CLEAR, and tell others likewise. **NEVER** assume that the current has been isolated – nothing can be regarded as safe until tested by a competent electrical engineer.

2.6.1. The Tram Track

Good foundations and ample drainage are keys to a well-built and durable tramway. Low frequency vibrations can be avoided by the incorporation of a rubber or polymer sandwich under and around the rails. This feature will also form an electrical insulator around the steel rails, thus providing a safeguard against "stray" return path current. Another precaution is to electrically bond all the steel reinforcing within the concrete tramway foundations, and so provide a kind of Faraday's cage. Electrolytic damage to parallel pipes and conductors was a regular feature on first generation electric tramways, where poor bonding and slack rail-joints exacerbated this problem. Today, some suppliers will coat the rails with polymer before delivery. Alternatively, some European operators prefer rubber extrusions fitted around the rails.

Specially rolled grooved-rail is normally installed on street tramways, though flat-bottomed Vignoles (railway-type) or other types of rail may sometimes be employed on reserved track. The shape of the rail can vary in cross section. Various sections (or types) of tram-rail were and are available. The first-ever British Standard Specification to be issued concerned the standardisation of tram rail, but these types of rail are no longer available and modern tramways utilise the German standard sections such as Ri 60 (the figure denoting the weight in kilos per metre). Modern tramway construction no longer employs fishplates at rail joints (other than when joining up rails with manganese steel points and crossings) – the rails are welded together (often by the "Thermit" process, see photo below) ensuring a quieter ride and good electrical continuity.

A photo of Thermit welding at Zülpicher Platz in Cologne, 1996.

Points come in various shapes and forms – left hand and right hand, but also equilateral turnouts (sometimes called parallel points).

Facing points are those with the point-blades facing the approaching tramcar, whilst trailing points are those which the tramcar would trail through from the opposite direction. Points may be sprung, so that the blades are kept in a particular position by springs. This is useful at passing places (often called passing loops) where in Britain the arriving tram will be directed to the left-hand track, and the departing tram's wheels will push the blades across against the springs which cause the points to return to the left-hand setting.

Diagram 12. A Passing loop with equilateral points.

Passing loops (see above). These can be laid in a symmetrical form using equilateral points (as shown), or in a safer form where the entry (i.e. facing points) is of a straight run-through form, and the exit is through curved track and points.

Some Tramway Junction Configurations

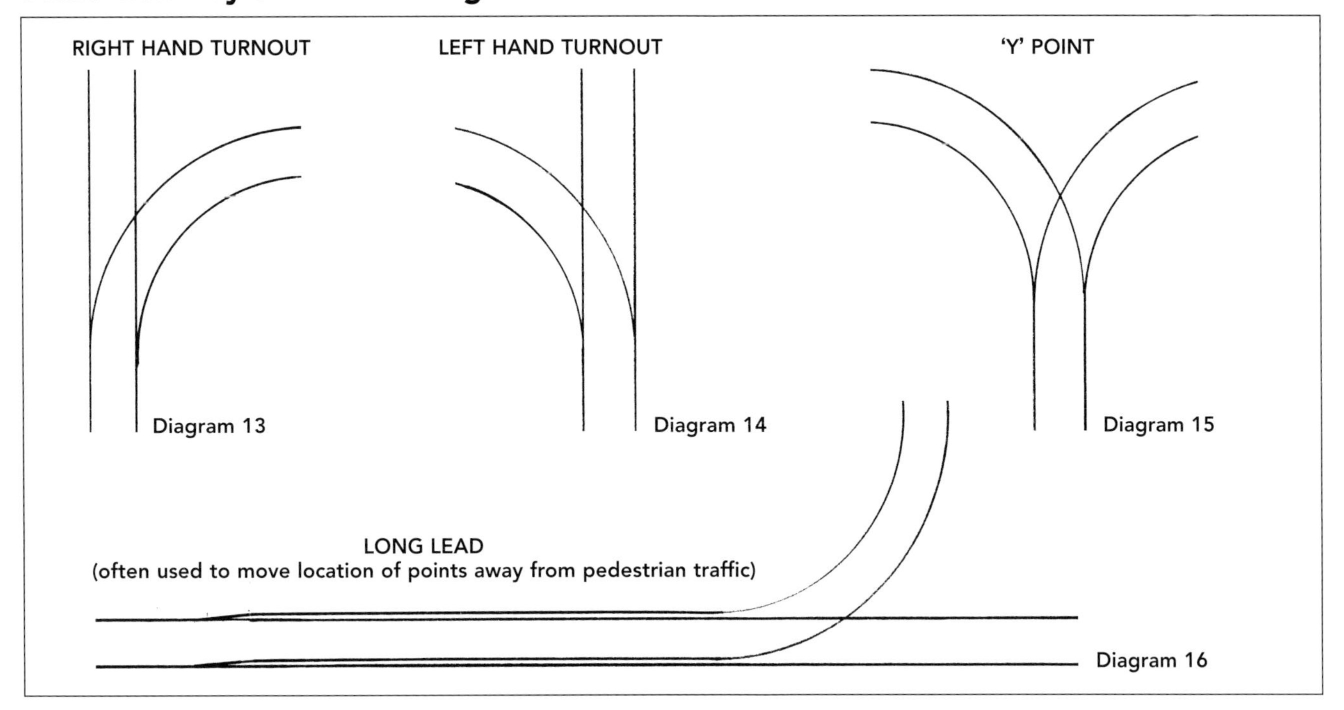

Crossovers

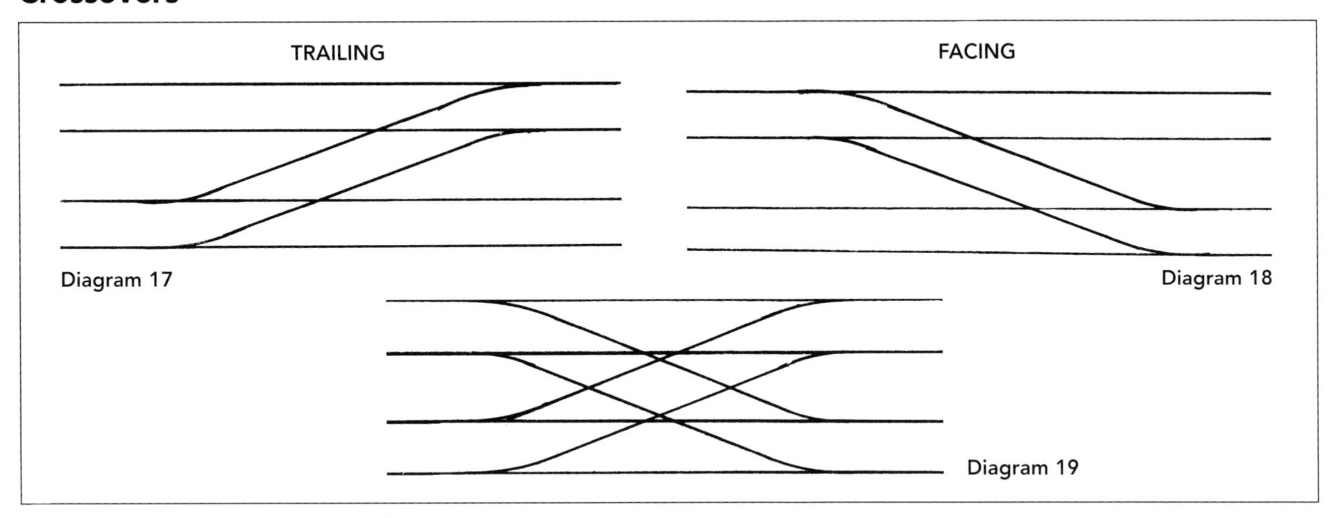

Junctions (typical examples)

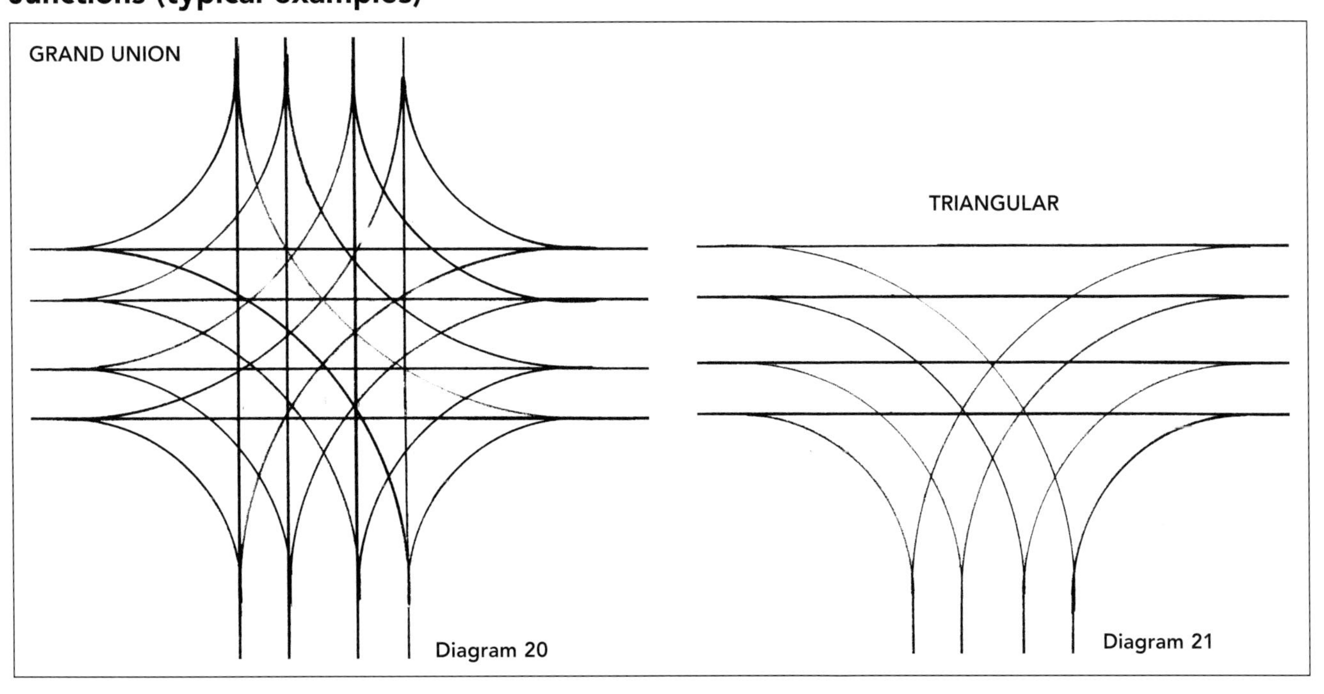

A crossover is the generic term for a track feature enabling trams on double track to change from one track on to the other – usually when reversing. Formed of two sets of points and a short connecting piece of track, there are two types: a facing crossover with the points facing the direction of oncoming trams, or a trailing crossover (opposite to that). In Gateshead and Blackburn some crossovers were installed within sections of interlaced track (see below) and saved the expense of two crossing castings at each crossover of this type.

A scissors crossover needs four sets of points and many crossing castings – being formed of a trailing and a facing crossover overlaid at the same location. It is useful at the mouth of a depot layout, or at a double-track terminus enabling trams to arrive and leave from both terminal tracks.

Electric points were introduced in Britain around 1914. These were actuated by the driver of the approaching tram by selecting power or coast (i.e. the controller switched to Off), during the time that the current collector passed a contact or skate on the overhead wire. This was no mean feat for the driver to hit the skate in the dark! At Ebertplatz in Cologne in 1968-9 there were two skates within ten yards of each other – drivers of cars wishing to go straight on had to coast through the first and power through the second skate! This system went out of use in the UK as the first generation tramways closed in the 1960s. In today's traffic conditions this system is deemed unsafe and is no longer approved. The power/coast system was unsuitable on gradients, Sheffield employing pointsmen at the junction of the Walkley route, who were provided with a sentry box as a shelter against rain up to the closure of that route in 1955.

Modern tramways use inductive systems called "Indusi" and "Vetag" to select the tram's route. With today's electronic gadgets it is now possible to programme in a specific route, so that each set of points encountered will be changed in accordance with the route set up within the electronics. With the human factor however, it has been experienced that drivers have overlooked point settings carried out automatically, and now most operators rely on their drivers operating a left or right switch when approaching the inductive point selectors.

Interlacing (railway equivalent: Gauntletted track)

This term denotes a section of track where, although two tracks are provided, the rails of one track are interlaced with the other. In effect a single line of tramway is the result, but the expense of point-work is avoided, as is the noise of sprung points returning after each wheel-set has passed! Interlacing is often used on modern tramways to enable points to be located away from pedestrians, a length of interlacing connecting the points with the diverging tracks some distance away. The name for this feature is "long-lead points". (See diagram 16)

Track lubricators are often installed just before curves to inject lubricant on to the sides of the flanges of tramcar wheels. Care should be taken to prevent lubricant reaching the wheel treads and thus compromising adhesion between wheel and rail. Some operators still use a water fountain (e.g. Rome, see picture below) to achieve flange lubrication and the avoidance of the unattractive squealing sound that tram wheels can produce.

Diagram 22
Interlacing.

Clearances

Clearances between tramcars and fixed structures, including poles, should be in accordance with Railway Safety Principles and Guidance, part 2, section G: Guidance on tramways, which stipulates the required clearances.

It is important to remember when passing an obstacle with reduced clearances, e.g., a parked vehicle that:

- On open sided trams, including the top deck of open topped trams, the passengers are informed not to exceed the boundaries of the tram. This can be enforced by the supervision of the conductor.
- The widest part of the tram may be the top deck roof and/or the saloon, i.e. not the driving platform, and do not forget driving mirrors at both ends. See diagram 23.

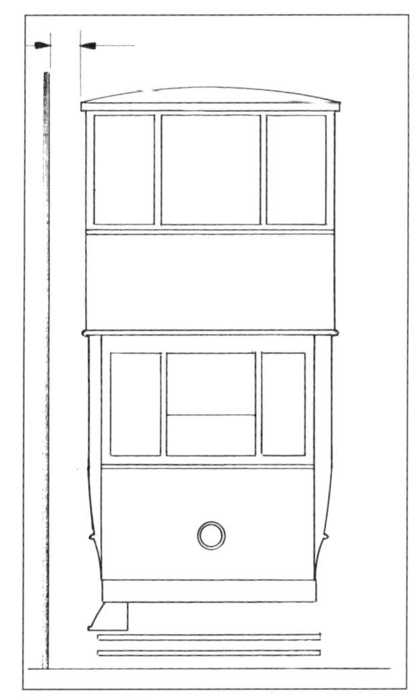

Diagram 23
Minimum clearance at top deck gutter.

Flange Running

If flange running is employed when a tramcar passes over points and crossings, the wheel tread is lifted from the railhead as the tip of the flange makes contact with the bottom of the rail groove. The bottom of the groove makes contact over a distance to prevent any shock loading and noise; this is done by preventing the wheel tread bumping over any discontinuation of the rail-head.

Diagram 26B shows a wheelset negotiating a single blade point; note the flange tip running on the dummy side and the wheel back face providing guidance by contact with the point blade.

The amount of clearance will be greatly influenced by the dynamic movement of the tram's springing. Low speeds produce less dynamic movement, so therefore drivers should always traverse limited clearances slowly. Trams are built to tolerances and these can affect clearances in extreme cases. Always keep checking in a close-fit situation, and if possible get a competent person to assist in checking clearances.

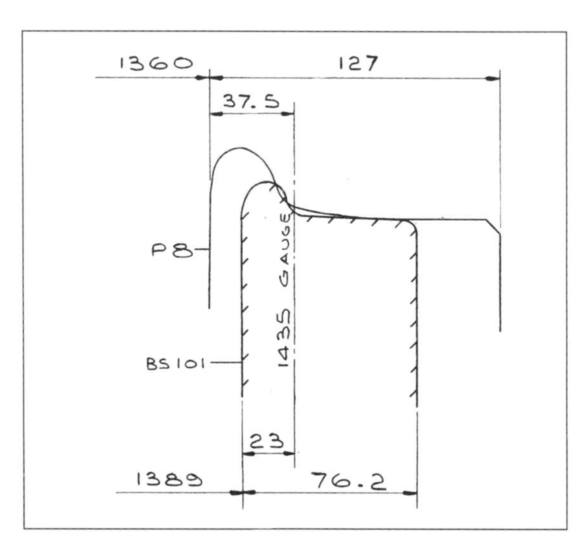

Diagram 24 (right)
A comparison between railway flange profile and the tramway standard – it is a reason why trams and trains cannot share the same track (in Britain anyway!). The smaller of the two wheels is a tram wheel made to the BS 101 standard. It is noticeably thinner, and the flange is both shallow and thin compared with the railway wheel. The dimensions are stated in millimetres. Drawings on this page by J.M. Shawcross.

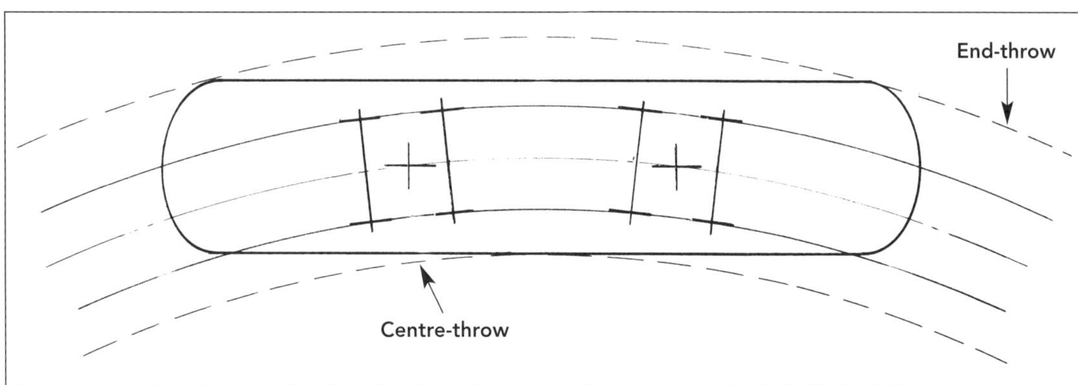

Diagram 25 (left)
How curves widen the tram's swept path. A tram on a curve will have a swept path produced by the end-throw and centre throw.

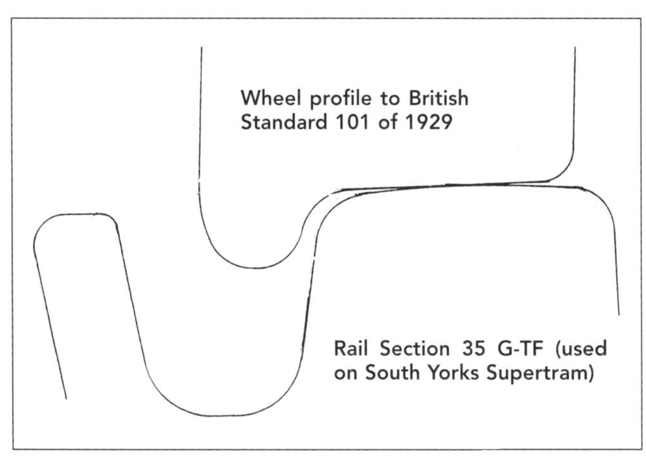

Diagram 26A
A first generation tram wheel profile on a second generation tram rail section.

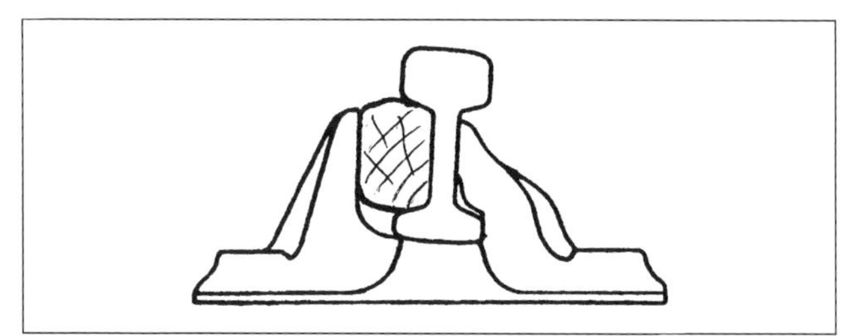

Diagram 26C. Bull head rail in chair with wooden key. This type of rail and fastening was universally employed on British-built railways until the 1950s when flat bottom rail began to be introduced. The Blackpool and Fleetwood tramway and London Underground railways are some of the last major users. This form of track is more costly to maintain, as frequent track inspections are needed to ensure that the tapered wooden keys have not worked loose. On the other hand it allows swift replacement of the rail – the keys can be knocked out in minutes – which was the reason for its popularity on the London underground system. Drawing J.M. Shawcross.

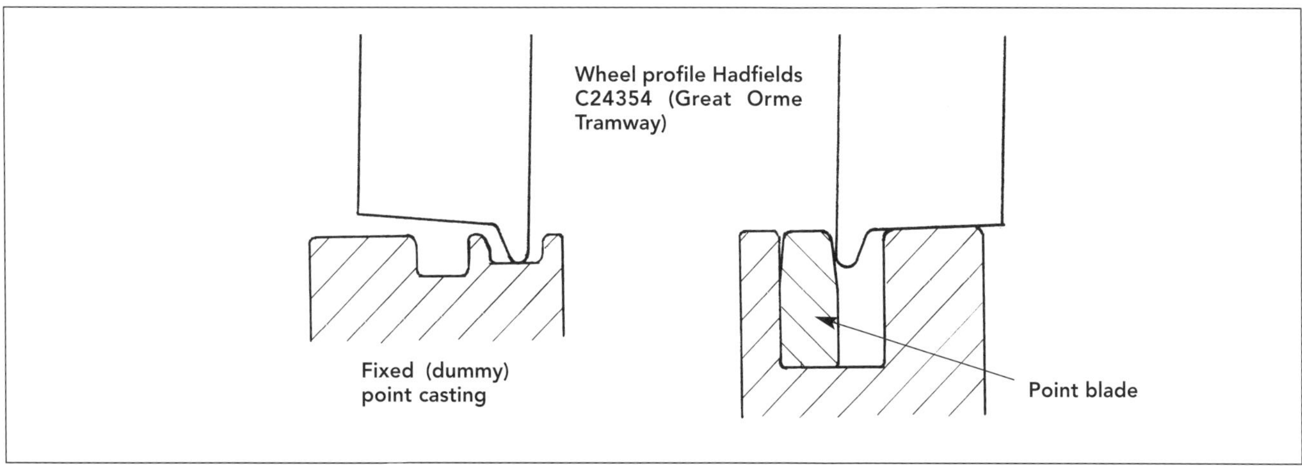

Diagram 26B
Note: The reduced rail contact can lead to reduced adhesion.

Part of the driver-training programme in Cologne involved the exercise pictured above and below. Trainees had to place plastic bollards at the boundaries of the swept path of a typical 2.5-metre wide double-articulated tram. Touching the bollards or being more than 15cm away from the vehicle counted as unsatisfactory. Notice the "end throw" of car 3874 above – the driver's external mirror being the widest part of the tram. The driving instructor (on the right) is watching carefully!

The location of these photos, Suelz depot, no longer exists, despite the building in 1968 of a new traffic office, as seen under construction in the photo below.

2.6.2 The Overhead Line Equipment

Poles, sometimes called masts, are the principal means of support for the overhead line installation. Poles, which are made of steel tubes, come in three standard sizes: A, B and C. A is for locations where the mechanical load is light. B is for medium loads, and C for heavy duty. A few English operators used lattice-work masts, but these are mainly found abroad. In town centres where buildings can support fixtures supporting the wiring, this is done by means of rosettes fixed to the walls of buildings.

Between the poles are strung span wires at right angles to the tram-track. On these span wires the ears are fitted which hold the trolley wire in place. Alternatively, where a single pole is deemed sufficient, a bracket arm may be fixed to hold up the contact or trolley wire.

Insulators of porcelain or modern insulating material are placed along the span wire, and are commonly fitted inside the suspension ear assembly holding the trolley wire. At least two insulators are required per span wire, although many operators installed three.

Trolley wire (or more accurately, contact wire) can be

In this photo of the double track junction at the Pleasure Beach, Blackpool, in 1958, can be seen the fittings and wire positioning for fixed head trolleys. The facing "frog" about to be negotiated by the leading boat tram is of the "pull" frog type. Note the short "golf stick" pull-off on the trolley wire, top left.

supplied in various diameters up to 100sq.mm. It is made from hard drawn cadmium copper. The wire can be produced in figure-8 cross section, or more common is the round section with grooves cut in the sides. Some former tramway operators with fleets of bow-collector equipped trams specified a cross section with a flat base, thus providing a wider contact area when new. Round trolley wire without grooves was available for use with clinch ears (see below).

An 'ear' is the generic title for the fittings which mechanically attach the trolley wire to its suspension fittings whilst maintaining an unimpeded path for the current collector. The oldest form is called a clinch ear, and has a copper attachment that is hammered around the trolley wire almost enclosing it. The drawback of this form of ear is that it does not provide a smooth surface under the wire. This can cause sparking with a trolley wheel, and at high speeds may damage the collector strip of pantographs. To improve on this the system of grooved wire and mechanical ears was designed. The mechanical ears are fitted with a claw of about 100mm length which is closed up by a number of screws, and firmly holds the wire by means of the two grooves cut into its cross section.

Frogs can be of the open type (only suitable for fixed head trolleys) with no moving parts. This sort of frog is usually installed just beyond where tracks diverge and the tram will already be exerting a pull in the direction that the trolley needs to follow. An open frog could be used by swivel-head trolleys in the trailing direction, but this type of trolley needs a frog with a movable blade when approached in the facing direction. Two types are used: a pull-frog, where the blade is held by a spring in the main direction, and when using the "siding" or branch a cord is pulled to move the blade in the chosen direction; the other form of frog is more elaborate. Called a poker frog or drop lever frog its direction is changed to the branch track when the trolley of the tram entering the curve displaces from the centre line of the straight track and brushes against the "poker". As the tram continues its path the trolley pole

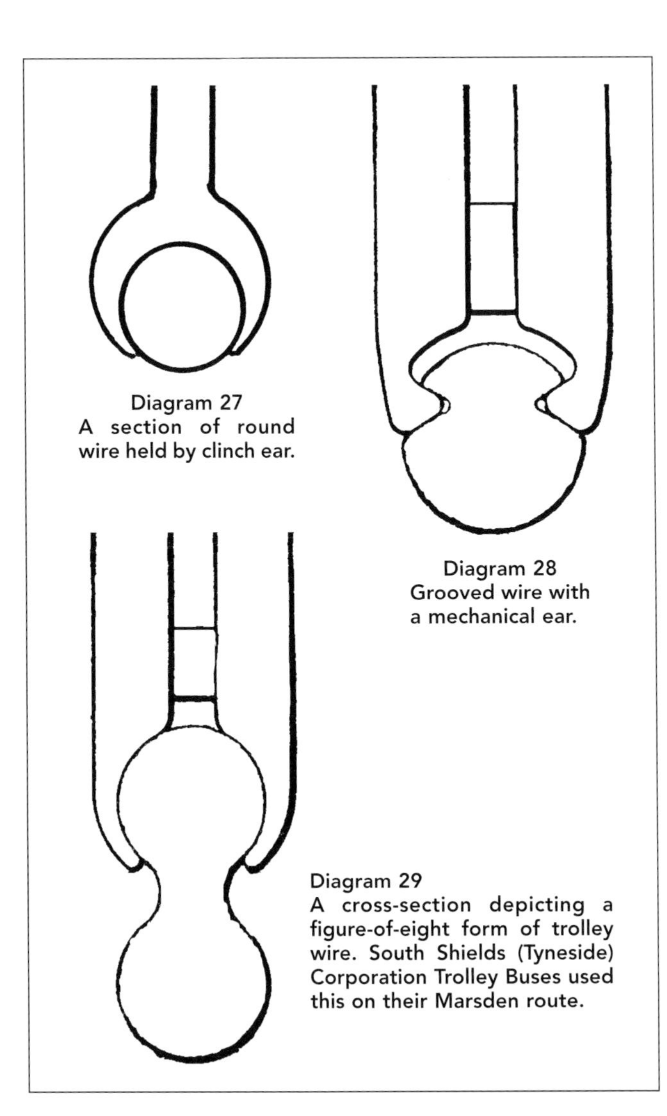

Diagram 27
A section of round wire held by clinch ear.

Diagram 28
Grooved wire with a mechanical ear.

Diagram 29
A cross-section depicting a figure-of-eight form of trolley wire. South Shields (Tyneside) Corporation Trolley Buses used this on their Marsden route.

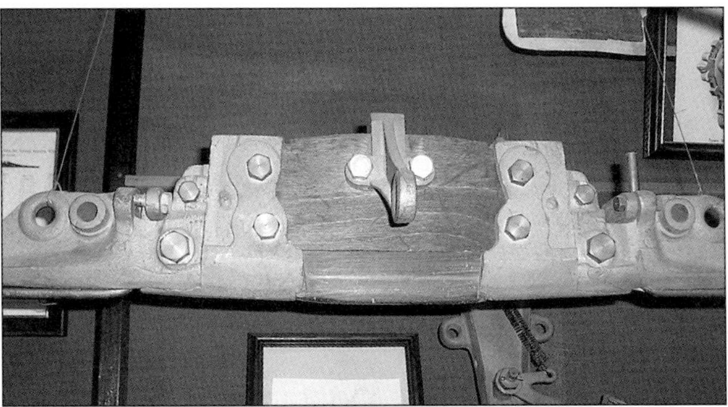

An early design of section insulator with wooden "dead" section dividing the two live parts. Drawing an arc when passing under this could shorten the life of this component.
Photo: J.M. Shawcross

causes the poker to move; this is connected by a kind of worm gear to the movable blade, the blade alters its position and the trolley is guided down the branch wire.

Contact skates have two forms: a simple one giving a passing signal to actuate a demand for traffic lights or single line signal system, and a more complicated design for use with power/coast point selection. This latter type detects not just the passage of a tram, but whether power is being drawn or not as the current collector passes.

A Section insulator is required every half-mile distance along the tramway. Primarily to enable the power to be switched off on any half-mile section, they also provide feeders where the power supply network connects into the tramway overhead line system. Whilst Britain's new tramways use section insulators designed for pantographs,

A wintry scene in Königswinter near Bonn, as a multiple formation of 8-axle cars is about to pass under a section insulator. Sadly, these wonderful bracket arms were later sacrificed in the Stadtbahn modernisation of this route.

and trams can be driven under them without the driver having to switch off power and coast; the older versions are much more fragile. Having a centre section which is electrically "dead", and made from insulating material (hardwood was used in the early 20th Century, see photo above), a tram travelling underneath and drawing power will cause an electrical arc. This can be sufficiently powerful to burn the insulated section. Furthermore, the interruption of power followed by the resumption of full voltage may cause serious damage to traction motors.

In the driving school of Cologne Transport in 1968 trainees who failed to switch off power at section insulators

Catenary installed on reserved track on the Amsterdamer Strasse in Cologne. Tensioning weights are suspended in the recess of the H-form girder mast.

Route 12 in Lisbon, 1983. The tram is negotiating what many tram enthusiasts called "Three Wheel Corner". The Guard Wires can be seen above the trolley wires. ***Photo: M.J. Henderson***

were "fined" the equivalent of 50p at today's prices – the proceeds being devoted to the beer kitty at the celebrations to mark the completion of the school course. The author was once visiting Frankfurt-am-Main when he happened to be standing close to a section insulator as a heavily laden double articulated tram was driven under it at slow speed. Drawing a large current the driver did not switch off in time, and the resulting arc burnt for well over thirty seconds, long after the tram had gone!

Catenary is more usually associated with heavy rail, but where speeds in excess of 30mph are permitted, the use of catenary on light rail routes is advisable to prevent loss of contact between the current collector and the contact wire. This frequently occurs on plain tramway overhead because of hard spots at places like bracket arms.

Catenary can take differing forms: compound catenary, as used on the former Manchester-Sheffield 1,500-volt DC railway electrification which had two levels of suspension; and simple catenary now almost universally used, where a catenary wire supports the contact wire by droppers every three or four metres. Often the catenary wire is of larger cross section than the contact wire. This feature provides additional current carrying capacity.

Guard Wire: for the sake of completeness mention ought here to be made of the requirement for this extra form of protection. Not seen in Britain after the First World War, it was a familiar feature of the Lisbon Tramway system until the 1980s when it was removed. Consisting of two un-insulated parallel wires strung 40cm above each trolley wire, and bonded to earth, its purpose was to protect telephone wires. In the event of one of these wires breaking, it would be caught and supported by the guard wires. Without this protection the telephone system could well be subjected to the 600V traction voltage (i.e. ten times its normal working tension.)

2.6.3. Current Collectors

Trolley poles are made from a tapered steel tube, and are usually covered with a layer of insulation. Older trams sometimes had a live trolley boom, but usually the steel tube was insulated and a cable run down inside the trolley pole to convey the current. Damage to the insulation – usually caused when a trolley dewires – must be repaired as a matter of urgency, especially on open-topped trams. The upward pressure on the trolley is maintained by springs at above 28lb.

An overhead line system can be designed for either fixed head trolleys or swivel head trolleys. The former consists of a trolley wheel that is fixed and unable to swivel in the vertical plane. The latter has a slightly smaller wheel mounted in an assembly providing a capacity to swivel, and so can follow an overhead wire that is not installed centrally over the track.

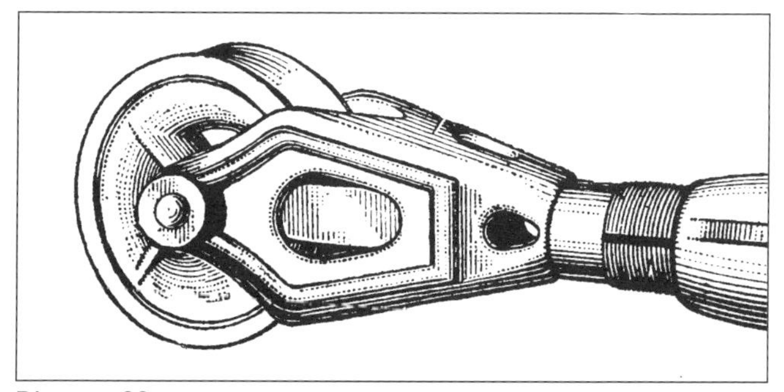

Diagram 30
A fixed head trolley assembly.

The carbon skid substitute for the swivel head trolley (more often used with trolley-buses) has a shoe in place of the trolley wheel, and this shoe is less prone to dewirement, but it tends to leave carbon deposits down the paintwork of the rear of vehicles so fitted.

Whilst an overhead line system can be designed for both fixed heads and swivel heads, if both are used a compromise solution is required which is not ideal for either! Fixed heads demand that the trolley wire is suspended over the centre-line of the track even on curves. Swivel heads are more versatile and the trolley wire can be positioned even outside the swept path of the tram. Under low bridges it used to be common to see the trolley head running parallel to the tram

A swivel head trolley assembly.

Leeds works car 6 (ex-Hull 96) shows off its bow collector on a murky day at Middleton siding (loop).

The motorman of Leeds City Transport "Feltham" 561 pulls the bow rope to prepare the car for reversal at Belle Isle crossover in 1956.

on a trolley wire strung alongside and at the same height as the tram roof.

On sharp curves swivel heads perform best when the trolley wire is positioned on the inside of a curve, the smaller radius reducing the sideways thrust likely to induce the trolley to leave the wire.

It can be seen from the above paragraph that requirements for the overhead installation vary according to the choice of current collector. This applies also where bow collectors or pantographs are used.

In order to allow bows to be swung over it was common practice to string a slack wire below the actual contact wire. Aberdeen used a special fitting to assist with bow reversal. With both current collectors (bow and pantograph) a zig-zag alignment is advisable, for a straight contact wire will cut a groove in the bow pan or carbon strip. Along with a compromise design of overhead where mixed types of current collector are in use, pantographs and bow-collectors may need under-running by-pass features where frogs (points) are installed. Mounted a few inches lower than the frogs and parallel to them, the under running by-pass provides a smooth path for the bow plate or pantograph head.

2.6.4 Signalling Equipment

Two purposes can be identified for signalling protection. Protecting single track sections of tramway was the most common, but as speeds of modern European tramways increased during the 1960s running on sight became more risky, especially when a tram became defective and stopped in mid-section. Where underground tramways were built automatic block signalling was compulsory. An automatic block is a system whereby a tramway is split into absolute sections, the signal at the start of the "block" preventing a second tramcar entering the section already occupied by a preceding tram. Two forms of signal were introduced in Cologne. The first a means of automatic block protection – after waiting for more that one minute drivers were permitted to pass these at red and run at extreme caution until two successive favourable signals had been encountered. The second type, located at junctions and other potentially dangerous locations, were designated "main signals" (Hauptsignale), and were not to be passed at danger. Although both forms of signal display were identical, reflective plates on the signal mast identified the type: white/yellow/white yellow/white for automatic block signals; and white/red/white/red/white for main signals. The addition of an automatic inductive train stop in the proximity of the latter signal was an additional encouragement to fully comply. If any 'spad' (railway parlance meaning Signal Passed at Danger) took place it was recorded instantly by the electronic equipment! Application too of the emergency track brakes also woke any slumbering passengers.

The use of signals is not something introduced by modern 21st Century tramways. Photographs survive showing semaphore signalling regulating the movement of trams around a blind single-track curve in pre WWII Bristol. Lisbon employed signallers or flagmen on the Graca tram route with quite primitive equipment. In the daytime a device resembling a table-tennis bat, and at night an oil lamp which could be turned to show one of two coloured aspects.

The token or staff system of regulating single line sections is the simplest and most reliable, and is often used in a temporary situation such as single line operation during track renewals. At the Beamish Museum tramline a railway type of electric token has been installed to protect one single track section. This is because being a circular line, not

This staff regulated a single line section on the Arnold route of the former Nottingham Corporation Tramways. It is now on display in the small exhibits section of the National Tramway Museum. *Photo J.M.S., courtesy NTM.*

A selection of signs displayed at the Thielenbruch Museum Tram Depot in Cologne. On the left panel the top three indicate Switch Off Power, Switch On, End of Overhead Wire. "W" indicates Electric Point's Skate (or Transponder). 'ME' stands for Magnetic Induction Transponder, and 'S' is a signal contact. Any sign with a red diagonal stripe means the termination of the indicated feature.

On the right hand panel are signs used on the interurban tramways. A white 'H' on a black background indicates where the front of the tram should stop. This often has a subsidiary board giving the length of the tram-train affected. The sign looking like a tunnel mouth indicates the limit of shunt. 'LP' instructs the driver to ring the gong and sound the horn. 'L' on its own calls for the gong alone to be used. The light and dark light bulbs indicate that car lighting is to be switched on (right hand) or off (left hand).

all movements are equally balanced – more trams may run clockwise than anticlockwise.

In the Sheffield of the 1930s, single line equipment on the Wadsley Bridge tram route, as well as at the tramway traffic lights at the end of the reserved track at Beauchief, used white lights showing displays indicating stop or proceed. This was in a form fairly similar to the high-tech tram signals used by the new generation of modern trams that glide through that city. Designers of both systems avoided the use of colours to prevent confusing motorists, this feature being a requirement of Department for Transport regulations.

To prevent confusion with railway signalling rules the Grimsby and Immingham Interurban Tramway, owned by British Railways, whilst using colour light signals to regulate single lines between passing loops, only used red and yellow aspects. No green aspect was used, as according to railway signalling principles, this would have indicated that the next signal to be sighted was showing a yellow (or green, if used) aspect, when in reality a red aspect could be expected.

On conventional tramways running "on sight" was and is almost the universal rule, with a single-line token or staff regulating the sections of single line that are too long to see from one end to the other. This is the simplest but most reliable form of protection.

The word "signal" in the German language includes not only traffic light signals, and colour light signals, but also the plates (often hung from the overhead wiring) giving information or commands. The German signals were standardised in 1937, though some local discrepancies still persist. Take for example the diamond shaped "switch off power" signal. This shows an electrical symbol of an open switch – two contacts and a bar below. Whilst identical with the railway sign giving the same instruction, this should be followed by a second sign showing a closed switch. This second sign marks the location where drivers may again apply power. Most tramway operators use the "switch off" signal to give warning of a section insulator, where of course it is mandatory to switch off power and coast through. In most of these cases on tramways, however, no "switch on" sign follows. Tramways in many parts of Germany avoid this ambiguity by using a letter 'T' instead of the electrical symbol. This initial stands for the word "Trenner" meaning Breaker.

Traditional tramways in the United Kingdom seldom used signs on a scale comparable with German operators. They did, however, paint poles with red stripes to indicate compulsory stops, and some operators put white bands on masts to highlight the location of section insulators. Compulsory stops could also be denoted on the passengers' "tram stop" board, or markings on the road surface, studs or other signage.

A higher degree of standardisation affecting signs and signals has come with the building of the new generation tramways. White light traffic signals for trams have even reached the Great Orme cable tramway at Llandudno, whilst the black and white diamond shaped signs giving information to tram drivers are now a common feature.

Traffic light signals for tramcar drivers are usually mounted alongside or above road traffic signals and are white on a black background to prevent misinterpretation by road vehicle drivers.

The signal can take the form of separate signal heads for each aspect or the current practice of a signal head with multiple functions, with rows of bulbs or LEDs (light emitting diodes) providing the bar and spot.

Modern light rail systems use sophisticated traffic management systems, or have access to the one provided by the local authority-owned highway management system. This means that approaching trams put in a demand electronically well in advance of their arrival at a road junction, and the traffic light sequence is amended to give the tram priority. Should a second tram approach within a given time no priority is given. At very busy road junctions during rush hour periods the tram may have to wait its turn!

Additionally, phasing can be linked to successive traffic lights. For example, trams leaving Nottingham's Old Market Square Northbound will only get a "proceed" signal at the bottom end of Market Street when the traffic lights at the top of the same street will be showing proceed by the time the tram reaches that location. This is designed to avoid a hill start on a steep gradient.

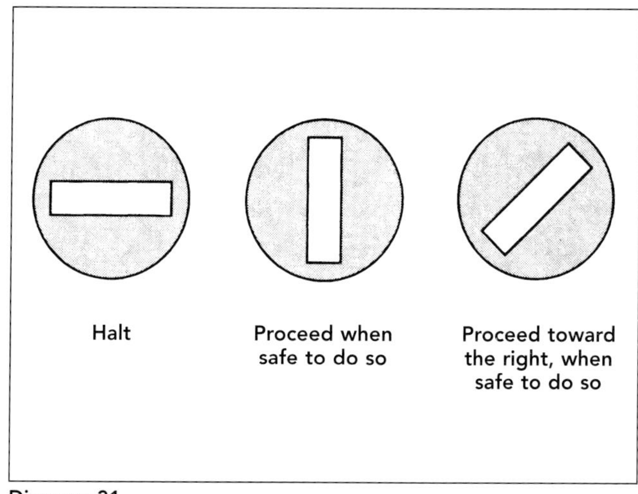

Diagram 31
Some of the aspect functions of tram signals are defined in the table opposite.

Modern Light Rail Signals

are defined in Appendix A of "Railway Safety Principles and Guidance", of part 2 section G, published by the Health and Safety Executive, HM Railway Inspectorate.

Signs are normally in black on a white background, although other colours may be permitted. A small selection is reproduced here:

Diagram 32
To indicate to tram traffic the requirement to stop, and not to proceed until it is safe to do so.

Diagram 33
This indicates the maximum permitted speed of tram operation, until it is amended by a subsequent speed variation instruction. The speed indication may be in mph or km/h.

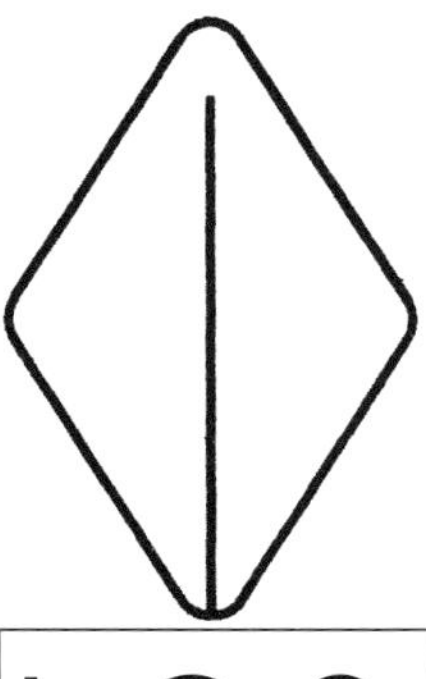

L.O.S.

(Limit of Shunt)

Diagram 34
This highlights to tram drivers the need to observe the instruction given on the plate fixed below or adjacent. The plate conveys a specific instruction to the tram driver. Often it may be the advanced warning of a speed restriction. A red diagonal line through lettering or numbers indicates the end of the previously stated instruction.

Diagram 35
To indicate to tram traffic the requirement to give way to other trams or other vehicular traffic.

Where it is possible to eliminate road traffic, the construction of a temporary crossover laid on the road surface enables tram traffic to continue operating, on a single track basis. Rostock, Eastern Germany, 2002.

A "Grand Union" junction in Berlin with temporary traffic lights displaying "safe to proceed", but only in one direction: i.e. ahead. The smaller mast and display indicate the point settings.

Until 1961 this was the workplace of Glasgow motor-men (and women) in winter and summer alike! No platform doors were fitted – as shown by newly restored 812 at Crich. *Photo: M.J. Henderson*

The main tram works in Lisbon showing a tram body lifted on jacks while the truck is replaced. The narrowness of the 90cm track gauge is apparent. *Photo: M.J. Henderson*

Newcastle 102 has its trolley turned at Wakebridge on the Crich tramway. Care must be exercised that all passengers remain seated during such an operation. *Photo: M.J. Henderson*

Blackpool and Fleetwood Tramroad car 2 on an enthusiasts' special near Rossall in 1960. This rural location is now a housing estate. The tram was one of the first to run at Crich. This car is fitted with an early form of fixed-head trolley.

Many of today's tram enthusiasts are blissfully unaware of the infrastructure that was wilfully destroyed in British cities in the 1950s. This photo of Halton estate (Leeds) shows high speed reserved track stretching beyond the horizon. Other cities too had miles of tramway like this.

CHAPTER 3

The History and Development of Tramcar Design

3.1 Improving the Brakes

The earliest design of tramcar relied on mechanical braking applied by hand to the wheel tread, and possibly also to the track (i.e. slipper) brake. From the earliest days of electrical science it was known that the direct current motor would also act as a dynamo. Although early designs of tram controller (e.g. the K series as used on the Manx Electric Railway, and until recently in Lisbon) were not built with graduated electric brake notches, it was possible to achieve electric braking by pulling the controller key into reverse. (This was not for the faint-hearted, and is not recommended except in case of a real emergency!)

The next stage in controller design was to overlap the "notches" for a graduated electric brake at the other side of the off position in what, when the handle was rotated in the power direction, were the parallel notches. Gateshead 52 in the Crich collection (at present in store) was fitted with controllers of this type. The advantage of this was to retain the larger separation of notches that the K series possessed, and so remain less prone to electrical flash-over than those controllers such as the B.T.H. B18 design built with a total of 15 notches!

During this era (the beginning of the 20th Century) the mechanical handbrake was improved by lengthening the swan-neck handle, and in some instances by mechanical improvements to the brake rigging such as cam operated levers. The most effective new design was called "Peacock Gear". This employs a device shaped like a cone which, fixed to the bottom of the handbrake column, gathers in the chain linked to the handbrake rods etc., as the chain wraps around this cone it moves to a more advantageous diameter thus exerting a stronger force. (See diagrams 36 & 37 on page 34.)

Eventually, in Britain and the USA the compressed air system was deemed supreme, even though some operators, for example London County Council Tramways, remained wedded to the electric rheostatic brake. In Britain the Potteries Electric Tramways were credited as the first major operator to fit air-brakes to trams. In their case it was to operate what today would be called "twin cars" – modified single deck four-wheelers coupled together. The advantage of fitting air-applied brakes enabled the driver to operate brakes on all the coupled vehicles, making for more effective braking.

On the mainland of Europe harsher winters and lower temperatures led to problems with compressed air systems freezing up. Many urban operators fitted solenoid-actuated disc brakes to their trailer cars. These disc brakes were fitted to the axles, and the solenoids (large coils) wired through jumper cables into the braking circuit of the motor tram. Any application of the rheostatic brake caused the solenoids to apply the disc brakes on the trailers, and this was in direct proportion – i.e. the stronger the rheostatic brake, the more force was applied to the trailer brakes.

As a safety precaution the solenoids were fed in parallel, not only each trailer being electrically connected in parallel, but also on the motor car a brake protection resistor was provided. This enabled the rheostatic braking circuit to function even after any of the brake jumper cables failed or became detached. It also provided for single operation of the motor car without needing any alteration to the wiring. With the brake protection resistance being permanently wired in, the disadvantage was that the final brake notch still had some resistance in circuit and therefore application of the hand-brake was necessary a little earlier than normal. Trams with this feature, when preserved for operation as a single car, are best modified to disconnect the additional resistance.

The possibility of coupling failure requires additional safety features, the earliest being a form of ratchet operated mechanical brake, two safety chains being fitted alongside the main coupling. In the event of the main coupling failing the safety chains would tighten and apply force to a ratchet device that would apply the mechanical brakes, and lock them on even if the safety chains eventually parted. More sophisticated devices came into use once batteries and low voltage track brakes were commonplace. An electrical contact mounted on the coupling, which was closed when the coupling was fully connected, would open in the event of the coupling parting. A relay would then apply the battery fed track brakes. An isolation switch was provided for couplings not in use.

Similar features can be provided where air brakes are used. Stored spring application of the mechanical brakes ensure full braking application even in the event of total loss of pressure in the air system. This system has largely replaced the older two-chamber braking system whereby a second pressure tank is constantly on stand-by. In the event of failure in the main system a pressure sensitive valve connects the reserve reservoir directly into the brake cylinders.

Interurban tramways soon recognised the economic attraction of running trains of motor-tram and trailers (in Europe as many as four trailers), but for urban trams rising speeds and increasing road traffic levels meant that the driver's job was getting more arduous on trams fitted only with handbrakes. Eventually in Britain during the 1920s air-brakes became a standard feature – even though some tramway systems were reluctant to spend the extra money needed. Leeds City Tramways built trams in 1928 that were equipped only with air track brakes – once on level track the driver was expected to use his muscles, as the mechanical handbrake was deemed to be the normal service brake. Having gone to the expense of installing compressors and the other hardware, it would have involved only a small increase in cost to fit extra pipe-work to use the air system for the tram's normal service brake.

3.2 Improving the Speed

As competition from the motor omnibus increased, tramway managers in the 1920s sought ways to retain passengers by improving the standards of comfort. Improvements such as installing upholstered seating on the lower deck (but not for the smokers upstairs!), fitting top-covers to trams and speeding up the timetable by increasing the acceleration and speed of the vehicles, were all part of this strategy.

Not all operators could afford new vehicles. One example of the make do and mend approach was Blackburn Corporation Tramways Department, whose electrical engineers were adept at modifying existing traction motors. Their modernisation programme had begun in 1923 by fitting top-covers to most of their fleet, and doing so in a way that would allow the modified trams to fit under the many low bridges in that town. Existing trucks were fitted with smaller diameter wheels, and to compensate for this the traction motor armatures were re-wound to make them rotate faster, and motors were also fitted with interpoles to improve the quality of commutation. Seven of the trams later received new and second hand motors of a more modern design, giving each tram a total of 140 horse power – surely Britain's fastest trams ever to be driven without airbrakes (or track-brakes), and with only the handbrake for service stops!

Traction motors have what is called a "balancing speed"; this means that on level track, irrespective of how long the driver holds the controller on the top notch, the speed will remain constant. If however the magnetic-field system within the traction motor is made less dense the armature will rotate faster. This is known as field weakening and the notch(es) on the controller are called the weak-field notches. What happens electrically is that the connections to the motor's field coils are made in parallel with a field-divert or "shunt". Often between 10% and 40% of the current is shunted. By 1930 this feature was employed to improve tramcar speeds, and was especially valuable on the reserved track tramways that were appearing in the new suburbs of cities like Birmingham, Leeds, and Liverpool. In the latter city the famous Green Goddess bogie-cars achieved speeds in excess of 50mph, until the expense of repairing burnt-out motors led to the disconnection of this feature. Speed sensitive relays fitted to 1960s continental trams barred the use of "weak-field" until a minimum speed was achieved, and this helped prevent motor damage.

Before we close this section, a brief mention of regenerative braking – another feature that received much attention in the 1920s and 1930s. Higher motor ratings and speeds obviously came at the price of higher electrical consumption, and bigger bills for the traction current! If rheostatic electric braking is used, the current generated in the motors is fed into the resistor box where it is converted into heat. Some astute operators fitted a special switch used at the colder times of the year to divert some of this energy into car heaters. This is only available if the rheostatic brake is used regularly, and the electric heaters can cope with the 1,000 volts produced by a hard application of the electric brake! Experiments in Aachen (Germany) in the 1930s proved that after the overhead supply was switched off on a section of double track tramway on a gradient, two trams allowed to descend the hill put enough regenerated energy back into the overhead to power one tram climbing the hill. Aachen equipped a number of trams with regenerative braking that remained in service until 1968 – the manipulation of the controller by the driver remained a puzzle to most observers!

Regenerative braking experiments in Glasgow were extensive, but the potential savings were deemed insufficient to warrant the considerable expense of modifying all the tramway supply sub-stations. The main problem at sub-stations being the question: What happens when no other trams are in the same section to use up the regenerated current? This is referred to as "receptivity", and older technology employed detector relays and a load bank to use up unwanted current. Lack of this receptivity caused at least one sub-station (in Leeds) to go into self-destruct mode when one tram experimentally equipped with regenerative braking was inadvertently rostered for the last journey of the day! The latest trams of Britain's new Light Rail systems all have regenerative braking, and on-board technology instantly detects any lack of receptivity, switching the current into braking resistors when necessary.

3.3 Interlocking Controllers and Brakes

Improvements to controllers, motors, and braking systems brought a negative outcome when drivers got things wrong. Simultaneous application of two braking systems acting on the same axles or wheels can quickly lock the wheels, with catastrophic results. Failure of a driver to fully exhaust the airbrakes can cause overheating of motors and resistors. To remedy these operator errors and shortcomings a system of interlocking cams and valves was devised. Mounted within a box fitted to the controller top, the shaft of the controller was extended to move cam-operated valves connected to the air system. There were a number of permutations depending on the variety of braking systems involved. Most interlock systems included an automatic sanding device – applying sand to the wheels whenever a hard emergency braking application was made.

The first type described here concerns trams fitted with air-wheel brakes, but only equipped with solenoid track brakes energised by the current from the rheostatic brake. In this form the interlock box on the controller top will dump the air in the air-wheel braking system whenever the power/brake main handle is moved beyond 'Off' into the emergency brake notches. This feature prevents locking of the wheels by simultaneous application of the air wheel brake and the rheostatic brake. However, whilst rapid rheostatic braking (along with solenoid track magnets) is effective in bringing the tram's speed down to nearly zero, the quick application of the handbrake is essential to hold the tram stationary. The Glasgow Standard tramcar had this feature, and driving this class of tram with a handbrake clipped out of use was a reportable offence in that city.

Glasgow's Cunarder and Coronation class tramcars enjoyed a reputation for speed and comfort. When the latter design emerged in the late 1930s they were hailed as the finest short stage passenger vehicles in Europe. Both classes had a multitude of brakes. As well as a hand-brake intended for parking, and air-wheel brakes designed for regular service use, track brakes were fitted. These were lowered by compressed air on to the rails, and the rheostatic braking current was then used to feed solenoids attached to the track brakes. On dry rails and at a moderate speed a stop within three tram lengths can be expected.

Effective braking was not the only improvement. To enable the work of drivers to become less onerous the familiar large 600-volt tram controller was dispensed with. Instead a small controller handled only 36 volts. The real work of switching the traction current took place in a special cabinet housing electro-pneumatic contactors. At an early stage in the commissioning of this and similar equipment

Glasgow "Cunarder" 1297 picks its way through the building site that would later become the Glasgow Garden Festival while on driver training duties in March 1988. ***Photo: J.M. Shawcross***

also in use in Liverpool, an Achilles heel was discovered – if either the battery or air-system supplying the switchgear failed, the equipment ceased to function, leaving a serious lack of braking capability. An Automatic Electric Brake (A.E.B.) modification was urgently designed and fitted. Once modified, any lack of air or control voltage caused a spring-loaded switch to operate and the power/brake changeover barrel to move into the brake position (unless it was there already). A warning buzzer would operate in the case of low air-pressure, but not before the automatic brake came into operation.

In the training of drivers on air-braked trams the need for vigilance concerning air pressure cannot be over-stated. Instructors drive home the message by isolating the compressor without warning, and waiting for the trainee to respond to the falling pressure registered on the air gauge. With these particular cars any slackening in their powers of observation results in the A.E.B. feature suddenly kicking in, and an unpleasant wake up call in the shape of the trainee's nose colliding with the windscreen!

Interlocking included in the Glasgow and Liverpool contactor-equipped cars not only prevented the air-wheel brake being used when the air-track and rheostatic brakes were selected, but also exhausted any air in either braking system once power notches were in use. Some operators (e.g. Leeds City Tramways) retained the capability of having the air-wheel brake applied while power notches were in use – this would allow drivers to restrain their tram under power for a short distance when on a falling gradient, in order to actuate the selector "skate" for electric points. Other tramway operators instructed their drivers to apply the handbrake for the same purpose.

Whilst most tramways had a separate motorman's airbrake valve (or a removable handle on the side of the interlock box) to apply or release the wheel-brake, Sheffield Corporation Tramways incorporated this valve into the interlock box and the cam-operated valves within it. Jokes abounded about Sheffield's one-armed drivers – their right arms being redundant!

The standard method of driving was concentrated on the main controller handle, operated of course with the left hand. Each side of the 'Off' position can be seen two dots cast on the controller top plate – one immediately before the first power notch to release the air-wheel brake, whilst on the other side of 'Off' the nearest dot denotes where the air-wheel brake is applied, the service air-brake being applied and released therefore by moving the controller handle. Heavy handed drivers should beware: turning the controller handle beyond the "Air apply" mark will dump the air in the wheel brake system as the equipment prepares for the assumed application of the rheostatic and air-track brake. Once this has happened it is advisable to stop the car on the air track brake, apply the hand-brake, and allow the air-brake systems to re-configure themselves.

Such complications as those described above are the downside of otherwise well intentioned interlock design features. So one can understand why many operators chose "straight" airbrakes instead. Without interlocking it is technically possible (though ill-advised) to simultaneously have the controller at full parallel and the brake fully applied.

The earliest motorman's brake valves are notoriously difficult to use. The "lap" position – i.e. the balance point between "apply" and "release" – being hard to find. Using an air-brake is like filling a bath with water. You let in the right amount, shut the tap and use what's in there. Then, when you've finished you pull the plug. In the same way, application of the air-brake means filling the system with sufficient air. Then you shut off the tap by moving the handle to the "lap" position. Finally, as speed diminishes you let out air to avoid the "nose-dive" which follows when drivers forget to feather the brake (i.e. reduce the air pressure before stopping). The Westinghouse Brake Company in the 1930s devised a system of self-lapping brake valves that are still in everyday use today.

A final note regarding air brakes: most air brake systems include an emergency brake valve primarily for use by the conductor, but available for use at the front of the tramcar also (the handles are not removable). The valve, when operated, connects the air directly from the reservoir into the brake cylinders. In doing so the pressure gauges may show a zero reading perhaps misleading the unwary. To reset the system the emergency valve must be closed, and the air released from the brake cylinders by use of the motorman's valve.

3.4 The PCC Car and Contemporary Developments

A radical new design of tramcar was introduced in the USA in 1929, being the result of years of research and development. Not only did the radical new design bring a renaissance to American urban railed transport in the 1930s, its influence was to extend world-wide, and can still be seen today. The American product remained beyond the reach of cash-strapped operators in Britain, but during the 1950s the Belgians could afford a few built locally under licence, and likewise the tramways in Den Haag, Holland; Madrid, Spain; and Rome, Italy; to name but a few.

Electro-pneumatic switchgear as fitted to Glasgow's Coronation class trams. The drum switch on the top right of the photo is the A.E.B. (see text above) which has to be disengaged manually in the event of the tram needing to be towed. ***Photo: Peter Ramsay***

The driver's switch panel in one cab of the 1929-built "Feltham" prototype M.E.T 331, now at the National Tramway Museum.
Photo: J.M. Shawcross

Leeds 602 at the Glory Mine terminus on the Crich tramway. The accelerator is housed inside the roof-tower, whilst additional rheostats are fitted fore and aft in the purple boxes on the roof.

3.5 Developments 1945-60

In England after World War II the PCC concept inspired two firms, Crompton Parkinson and Allen West, to devise something similar – but not too similar in case American patents were infringed. The British exercise didn't really involve the PCC tram as an overall design, just the main equipment: accelerator (a form of combined switchgear and resistor bank), the resilient wheeled trucks, and cardan shaft drive.

Blackpool eventually ordered a total of thirty-nine sets of propulsion equipment including VAMBAC accelerators (i.e. Variable Automatic Multinotch Braking and Acceleration Control). This meant that no longer did the driver have the familiar brass (controller) handle to turn, a joystick replaced this. Pushing the stick forward selected the rate of acceleration, pulling it back determined the rate of braking. The final position in this braking sector was an emergency one which applied the track-brakes.

The resilient wheeled trucks supplied by Messrs Maley and Taunton of Somerset included not only rubber sandwich inserts, but also traction motors mounted at right angles to the axles, which delivered power through a cardan shaft and hypoid gears. Whilst the PCC concept was usually an all electric specification, Blackpool Transport played safe and fitted airbrakes to its VAMBAC cars.

Glasgow experimented with arguably the only double deck single-ended PCC ever built (except that purists wouldn't use the PCC label!). Numbered 1005 it was fitted with equipment similar to that used in Blackpool. Unlike the Blackpool cars which, being single deck, had the accelerator mounted at the base of the trolley tower, this double-decker had it fitted under the rear platform. As the equipment (like most PCCs) used a permanent parallel connection of the traction motors, the starting current was high and so the amount of heat dissipated in the accelerator's resistors was rather high too. Ventilation was all important, but the more holes provided for air current cooling meant the more water spray ingress took place when it rained. Eventually, car 1005 was rebuilt to resemble a double-ended Cunarder and the VAMBAC equipment removed.

Last, but not least, Leeds City Transport bought two state-of-the-art single-deck trams in 1953 – this being Coronation year these two rail-coaches (as they were officially called) appeared in a livery of royal purple, and were numbered 601 and 602. Both similar in appearance, 601 had conventional traction equipment, but car 602 was the closest to the PCC concept of any British tram. Instead of air-brakes to hold the car, battery-fed solenoid stored-spring brakes were fitted. This tram was indeed an all-electric version, but sadly its commissioning programme was incomplete when the decision was made to abandon tramways in Leeds.

As this and its sister were intended

An accelerator as fitted to the Czech-built PCC equivalent design.

to be prototypes for the renewal of the entire tram fleet – which was to go hand in hand with the modernisation of the tramway system in that city – car 602 became an embarrassment to the Transport Committee. Today it remains in existence at Crich Tramway Village as a reminder of what might have been possible.

Sadly, Leeds has not fared well in its hopes of a tramway renaissance in recent years. Despite years of planning and expense invested on preliminary works, the government has refused to provide any funding on the grounds that the projected costs are way above the original budget.

3.6 The Latest Generation

Following on from the 1980s success of the Tyne and Wear Metro and the Docklands Light Railway – both of which were light railways with no street running, but used vehicles with propulsion equipment based on German tramway practice – the Metrolink project in Manchester was opened in 1992. Although most of its route length is along former heavy rail suburban lines, at its centre is a Y-shaped street tramway linking two important railway stations and bringing the new trams into the central area of the city. This makes the former suburban railways more attractive to tram passengers. An extension to Eccles followed in 2002, and today passenger loadings are so high that the tram fleet is barely able to cope. The chosen design of tram is based on Italian tramway technology and has all the right sound effects.

South Yorkshire Supertram. This time the choice of tram builder was the well-known and much respected Siemens/Düwag factory in Germany. The trams have achieved a record of good reliability, and with gradients of 10 percent to climb – the installed horsepower totals around 2,000hp per tram – all axles are driven. Sadly, whilst the vehicles were a success, the route planning and usage forecasting fell short of the mark. A pre-pay and validate-before-use system of ticketing scared away passengers in the early days, and the lack of through ticketing with other modes of travel made for expensive journeys. Sheffield has had a multi-coloured selection of bus operators since local transport was de-regulated, and the offer of a ride to town on a twenty-year old bus at half the fare charged on the multi-million pound tram was too much of a bargain for price conscious Yorkshire folk. Eventually, the Supertram operation was sold at a knock-down price to the Stagecoach group, and their sensible marketing and ticketing policies have considerably boosted passenger figures.

Next to open was the Midland Metro tramway. Sadly, nothing was learned from the Manchester experience and the choice of tram design again went to Italy. The sound effects emanating from the street running section in Wolverhampton would be useful if one was belatedly recording sound effects for an 8mm film of a first generation tramway.

With both South Yorkshire and Midland Metro eventually giving up pre-paid ticketing and introducing tram conductors, many people expected the next new tramway Croydon Tramlink to follow suit, but it didn't! Tickets have to be purchased before boarding. Opened in 2002 a wise decision was made to purchase a German design of tram – of which 120 have been built for Cologne (by a factory in Belgium!). The passenger loadings have been good from the beginning – so much so that Croydon needs additional trams!

Nottingham Express Transit is Britain's latest new tramway. It opened in March 2004, and is the first new generation tramway to employ conductors from the outset, though the trams are equipped for one-person operation. The first year's statistics showed that the annual passenger total was 8.5 million customers – a half-million more than the

The tram driver's cockpit Cologne 1962 style (with later additions). The controller's cam-operated switchgear is in the cupboard to the left. The lever with the black knob (a dead-man device) is pushed forward for the power notches, and pulled back for the brake notches – the red arrow highlights the 'Off' position – and drives the mechanical contacts via bevel gearing. On the shelf below the windscreen are the controls for radio and stop announcements. On the main control panel can be seen from the left: switch to release main circuit breaker, red warning lights for battery voltage and resistance notches, speedometer, battery voltmeter, door and passenger stop request control lights, and trafficators. The handle to the left of the white notice controls the solenoid brakes when moved upward, and two "notches" below the off position are: 1 rail-brakes, 2 ditto with sand and warning gong. Along the bottom row are switches that operate: sanders, loudspeakers inside or outside, doors, and the blinkers. The column on the right is the hand (parking) brake, and out of sight on the floor, four pedals provide controls for headlight main beam, gong, horn, and alternative dead-man feature.

predicted total. Here, like Croydon and Manchester, additional trams are urgently needed. How unfortunate therefore it is that all three systems require trams of varying shapes and sizes, thus precluding the placing of a shared order. Nottingham uses 2.4-metre wide 100% low-floor trams, the other two operators, trams of 2.65-metre width, but Manchester does not use low-floor types, and Croydon trams have 85% low floor access.

A year or so ago the Incentro type of tram, chosen for Nottingham, was only used in one other city – Nantes in France. Designed by an Adtranz factory in Germany, it was seen as not fitting in the portfolio of new owner Bombardier, after Adtranz was taken over by Bombardier. However, it may yet see a renaissance, for problems with competitor Siemens' widely sold "Combino" articulated tram resulted in new orders going elsewhere, and a boost for rival Bombardier products. A further order in 2005 from Nantes for more "Incentro" trams was fulfilled at their factory at Bautzen in Eastern Germany. One such tramcar was demonstrated in Berlin during March 2005, and with a large number of Berlin's Tatra trams needing replacement, a large order is pending but the choice may go to one of five competing designs.

Millions of pounds have already been spent in detailed design work for an additional two lines for Nottingham. This time the government cannot use the excuse of tramways being a poor investment, for Nottingham's line 1 has outperformed the predictions (the latest figures show that almost 10 million passengers were carried in the twelve months to March 2006) and investors are keen to proceed. With no other new tramways in prospect for England, all eyes are on Nottingham for the future.

A glimpse into the future would not be complete without reference to the future generation of tram drivers and their training. Following the identification of shortcomings in driver training programmes provided by a minority of railway companies, a government-led initiative has produced plans for a nationally recognised and accredited (rail) driver-training syllabus. Successful trainees will be awarded an NVQ. Specific local features and route knowledge will be extra to the standard syllabus.

Not long ago I was privileged to experience 21st Century training facilities in Berlin. The Transport Department in that city has invested heavily in supporting their driving school. It has the use of one of the few tram simulators ever built. This remarkable machine lives in a seven-metre high building resembling a film studio. In an adjoining room behind a glass partition sits the driving instructor surrounded by monitors which replicate the trainee driver's view. Six tram routes were filmed and digitalised. These provide the street scenes along which the simulated tram passes. At the click of a mouse the instructor can introduced various hazards and potential accidents. The trainee has to react quickly and effectively. A white van may appear from a side street and pull out into the main road without first stopping. Then, while drawing up to a set of traffic lights, a large petrol tanker overtakes and stops within the tram's swept path!

Anyone who has experienced just twenty minutes on the simulator will tell you that it is more stressful than driving a real tram. The reality is enhanced by the use of a real driving cab (two are available for use – one from each major type of tram) and this is supported on hydraulic stilts. As the tram simulator appears to move, these replicate the jolts and movement of turning corners and traversing points. Naturally, the sound effects are accurately reproduced too.

This simulator, which is based on training modules for air-line pilots, consists of a tramcar cab mounted on hydraulic stilts. Through the open door at the top of the steps can be seen the windscreen. When the cab door is closed the steps move away, and the trainee is very much on his/her own! But communication is provided between trainee and instructor by an intercom.

Photo of the exterior of the simulator module viewed from the rear at the opposite side to the cab unit. The powerful hydraulic stilts can be seen. These give life to the cab, so with the virtual reality panorama screen, and sound effects the illusion is almost total.

The control room with the instructor's desk, above which are mounted monitors replicating the moving street scene as seen by the trainee in the cab's panoramic screen. The lower monitors present a real-time depiction of how the electronic "tram" is performing (e.g. powering, coasting or braking, and most importantly any wheel slip or slide). It also indicates other control functions which are repeated as shown on the driver's desk.

CHAPTER 4

Operating the Equipment

4.1 The Tramcar and its Fittings

Where heritage tramcars are concerned the fact that almost all the on-board equipment is life-extended must be a paramount consideration amongst staff. When components wear out replacements will need to be specially made. Handling the equipment sensibly and gently will prolong its life, and not lead to tramcars being out of service for long periods while spare parts are procured. This also means avoiding any excessive speed and/or rates of acceleration or braking – the certain causes of inducing stresses in the bodywork.

Attention may now be given to the ergonomics of the driving cab or platform. This will be the driver's workplace for eight hours, and it is important for his/her wellbeing that all adjustable items are at their optimum setting. Where provided, seats should be positioned so that all controls are within the driver's reach, but not too close that a swift evacuation of the cab is hindered – this being the driver's escape route in the event of an impending accident.

Cab doors should be kept closed, and no luggage allowed to impede the access or exit. No unauthorised person should be allowed to ride in the cab or on the driving platform.

The controller is best operated at a close range by standing close by. Here is my recommendation. First position your body so that with a straight left arm your hand is on the knob of the controller main handle. Then, by moving your body forward slightly and bending the elbow, this will allow you to move your forearm in a clockwise motion, and with it the main power handle to the first notch. Repeat this through the notches and gain acceleration. If at any time the controller is to be switched off, swinging your forearm in an anti-clockwise direction and rapidly returning your arm to its straight line position will enable you to reach the 'Off' position in one clean movement.

Switching off briskly limits the time during which the arc formed between the opening contacts will burn. Hitting each notch accurately will also prevent burning of contacts within the controller. When using power, never notch backwards except to 'Off'. When using the electric brake notches do not notch backwards, even when it is realised that too much brake is taking effect. First allow the braking effect to subside as the speed drops, then move the handle smartly back one notch. Drivers should remember that there are only three notches whose use is unlimited: Off, Full Series, and Full Parallel. All others will cause overheating of the resistors if used for more than 20 seconds.

Drivers should keep their hands on the two main controls of a tram: the left hand on the knob of the controller main handle, and the right hand on the hand-brake. If the left hand is not on the knob of the controller, the driver is most ill-prepared for any emergency stop which may become essential. The knob is made from insulating material (wood or Bakelite) and offers additional protection against electric shock in the event of a short-circuit within the controller.

Voltages much higher than the normal traction voltage are generated during electric braking, therefore, drivers

Prague in May 2002. The driver's elbow is slightly bent ready for notching up from the 'Off' position on the controller.

The driver of Chesterfield 7 at the National Tramway Museum demonstrates the correct way to handle the controls. His left hand is on the knob of the controller power handle. His right hand is on the brass swan-neck, brake handle – which is well positioned for a "ready to wind in" action.

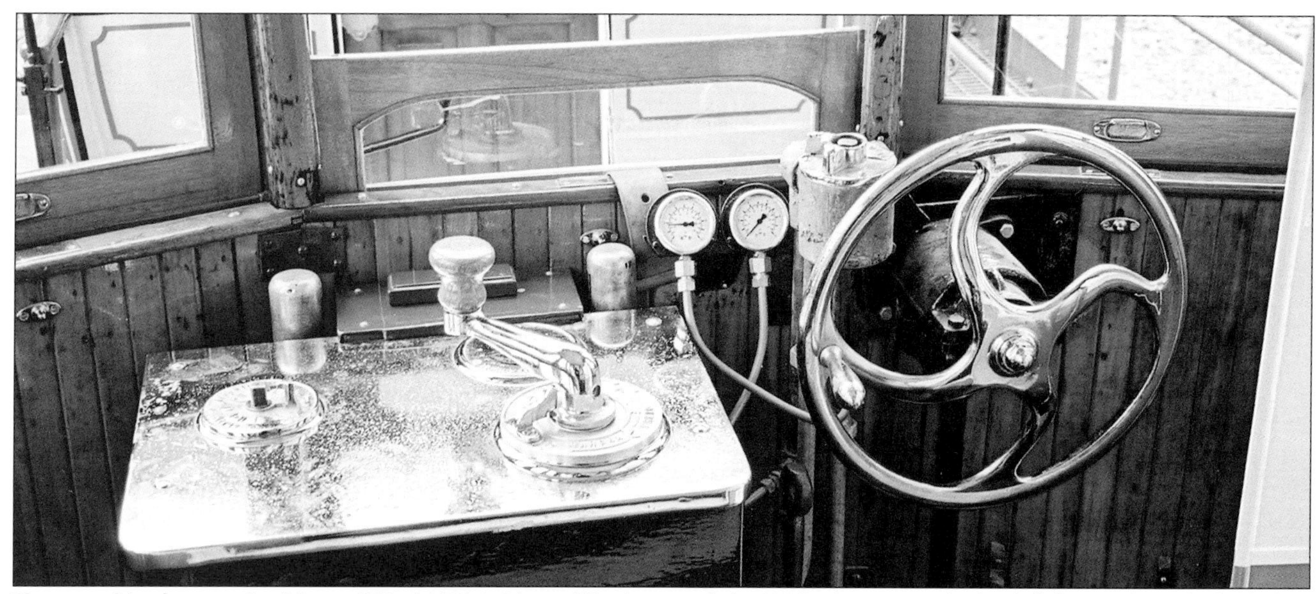

The tram driver's controls of Porto 273 of 1928 (with modifications made in 1964), showing at the back (left to right): a lockable box securing the trafficator switches, left hand air gauge shows reservoir pressure, right hand gauge indicates the pressure in the brake cylinders, and to the right of it at the back the motorman's air valve (with handle removed). A controller designed in the 1950s (straddled by two lamp housings to provide enough night illumination) and a vertical hand-brake wheel complete the picture.

should never return the main controller handle to the Off position from any braking notch until the braking effect (and the high voltage it produces) has diminished.

Unless the tramcar is designed for repeated use of the electric brake, the electric brake must only be used in an emergency – except when testing the brakes as part of the start-of-day checks.

In the event of a failure in the controller's normal electric brake facility a full application can be achieved by the following procedure. First return the power handle to 'Off', trip the main circuit breaker, move the controller key to the 'Reverse' position, and then move the power handle to the first 'Parallel' (power) notch. (In an emergency hit any parallel notch.) Beware – this is a full brake application and can be very fierce.

There were few hand-brake fitted trams with a vertical wheel, the majority being fitted with the familiar brass swan-neck assembly (see diagram below). Some trams were equipped with vertical wheels, among them being those built by the Great Central Railway for use on the Grimsby and Immingham Tramway. They were the last to operate in Britain using a vertical wheel for service braking, until the line closed in 1961.

The brake column supporting this also transfers the applied force to a second ratchet at floor level. This ratchet engages a pawl (or dog) which can be nudged into place and held there by the driver's right foot. (Tram drivers should always wear robust shoes!) The brake is applied by turning the brass swan-neck and locking the force into the braking system by use of the foot applied pawl. Should it be necessary to apply greater force the driver can turn the brass swan-neck in an anti-clockwise direction – the in-built ratchet will allow this – and re-application in the clockwise direction will increase the braking force being applied.

Drivers should try and discover the neutral position of the handbrake system (especially after changing ends) by lightly applying the brake, noting where it begins to "bite", and then releasing the brake-handle a quarter turn. If you hold the brass handle with your right arm extended, rapid application of the brake can be achieved by pulling the swan-neck towards oneself. Then with your body at a right angle to the swan-neck the use of your body weight to pump against the handle, each time locking in the force by means of the foot operated pawl, will achieve optimum braking.

Care must be taken not to wind on the hand-brake after the air-brake has been applied. Doing this will lock the

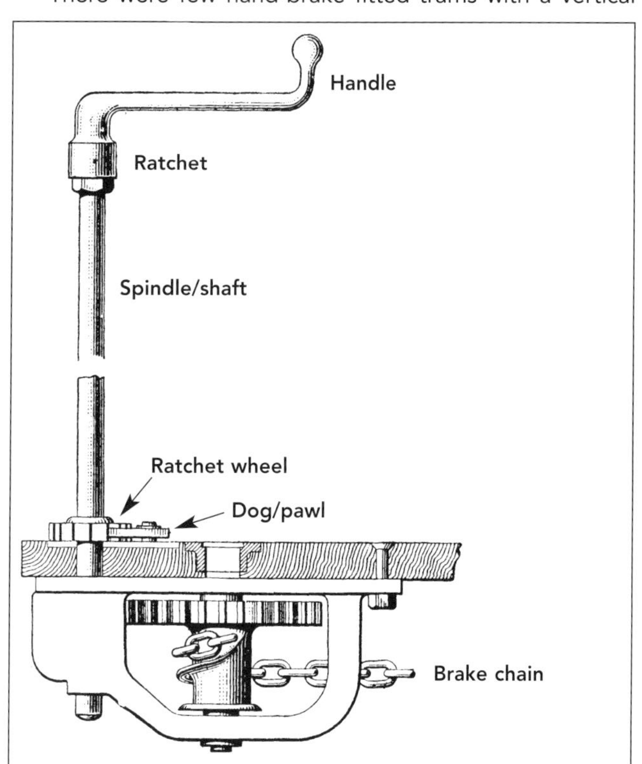

Diagram 36
A quick acting handbrake, commonly called "Peacock Gear".

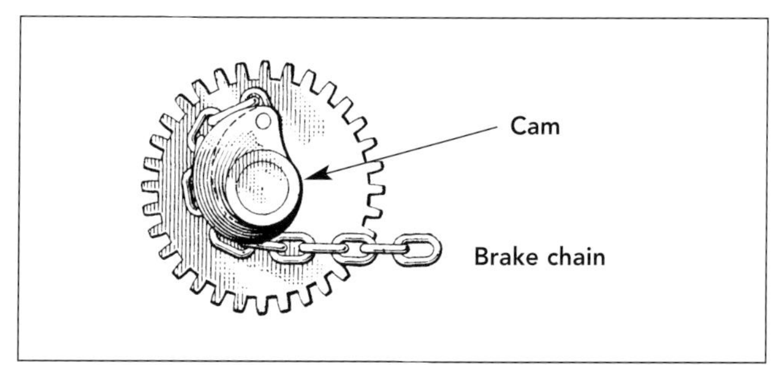

Diagram 37
View of cam wheel from underside.

equipment so tightly that the braking system will be seized in the fully 'on' position.

Care therefore, must be taken to release the hand-brake fully before the air-brake is applied. Unless this precaution is taken the air-brake – when next released – will cause the heavy brass swan-neck handle to fly around at great speed and force. Countless accidents resulting in drivers suffering broken arms have been the outcome of persons failing to observe these precautions when using the two braking systems. Mixing, or what is called compounding, the two is very dangerous and should be avoided. Never allow the brass swan-neck handle to fly around, and where restraints are provided, these should be used to anchor the brake handle – at all times on the rear platform, and when the driving platform is left unattended.

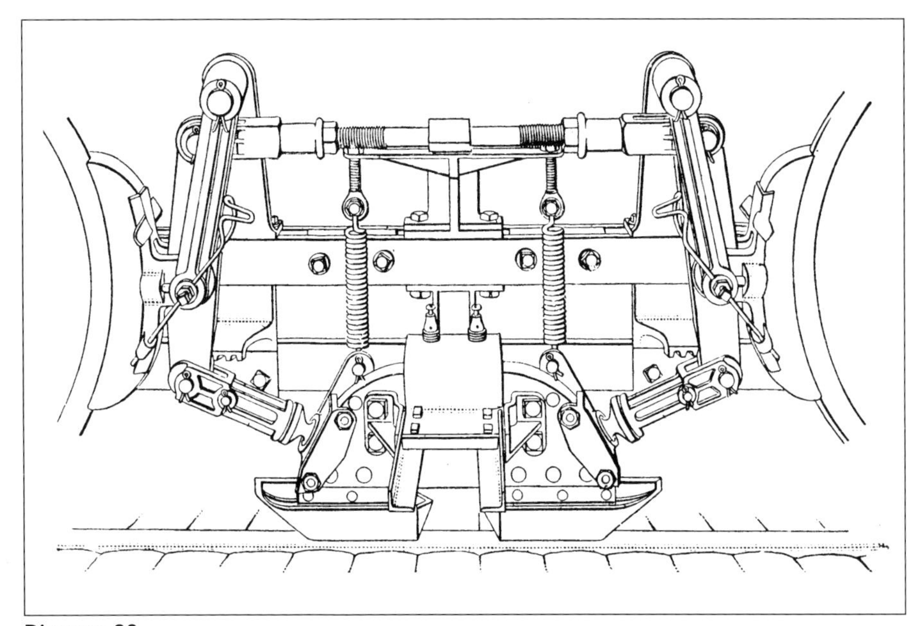

Diagram 38
This drawing shows an electro-magnetic track brake with mechanical links to the wheel brakes. As the solenoid brings the shoe down onto the rail, linkage causes the wheel brakes to be applied (left and right).

Pedals must be in place before any tram is moved. (Some are taken from one platform to the other, some are designed to disengage by being rotated 90 degrees.) Often the gong and sand pedals are adjacent and are best operated by the heel of the tram-driver's shoe. The lifeguard resetting pedal can frequently be awkward to operate – often a forward push before depressing it will succeed.

Rear-view mirrors may need adjustment. Remember to retract the outside ones when leaving a driving cab or platform. Finally, your peaked hat is both an essential sun shield and provides protection against exploding circuit-breakers at head-top level. Do not drive without this uniform item.

4.2 Low Voltage and Compressed Air Systems

Many trams built after 1930 were equipped with low voltage systems. This provided electrical power at a more suitable voltage for headlamps, emergency lighting, power doors, etc., all independent of the traction supply. The power source was a battery that was kept charged by a motor-generator (i.e. a 600V motor driving a 28-volt generator) or, on more modern trams, by a static converter (i.e. an electronic device with no moving parts). An alternative method of battery charging was by using the negative connection from the compressor so every time the compressor motor ran, the current flowed through the battery before it returned to earth. Vigilance is essential for drivers to be aware of low-voltage warning lights where fitted, or battery voltmeters showing a low reading. Drivers must know the location of the battery isolation switch and use this to cut off the battery in case of fire. Solenoid track brakes are often battery-fed and therefore must be used only for a short time to prevent draining the battery.

The first Coronation class tramcars in Glasgow utilised the low voltage system for a public address installation. This was soon disconnected following incidents when drivers made unflattering remarks about the driving competence of others, to a wide audience of all the passengers, after forgetting to switch off their microphone! Any microphone should only be used when the tram is stationary.

Not only do brakes form part of a tramcar's air system, but also windscreen wipers, sanding equipment, doors, and whistles. Pneumatic switch-gear uses a sizeable quantity of air. Where trams are fitted with this equipment a separate low-pressure warning and/or cut out is essential to prevent damage to the air-powered contactors in the event of low pressure. (See Chapter 3 on page 29). If an air leak is suspected all these areas should be checked out.

Door operation is often actuated by compressed air, but controlled by electrical valves and push buttons on the driver's desk. Where power operated doors are not under automatic control, drivers must first check in their mirror(s) that no one is likely to be endangered by the door-closing sequence. Doors should only be opened at authorised stops.

Air sanding can be remote controlled. A jet of compressed air and sand is fired at the wheel/rail interface.

Compressors have not always been powered by an electric motor. At the turn of the twentieth century axle-driven compressors were often fitted. Drivers need to drive such heritage trams with extreme caution when running out from the depot. Until such time as the pressure has built up fully, only the hand-brake and rheostatic brake are available for use.

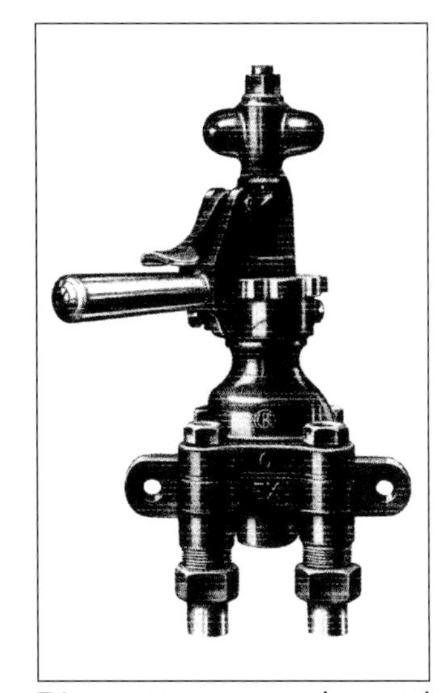

Trigger to operate the sand ejectors is located above the brake valve handle.

Pressure in the system charged from an axle-driven compressor is regulated by a valve similar to the safety valve fitted in a conventional system. The interurban trams belonging to the Innsbruck Tramways in Austria built in 1909 (four are now preserved) were fitted with axle-driven compressors on account of the two voltages used (600 volts in the urban area, and 1000 volts on the inter-urban routes).

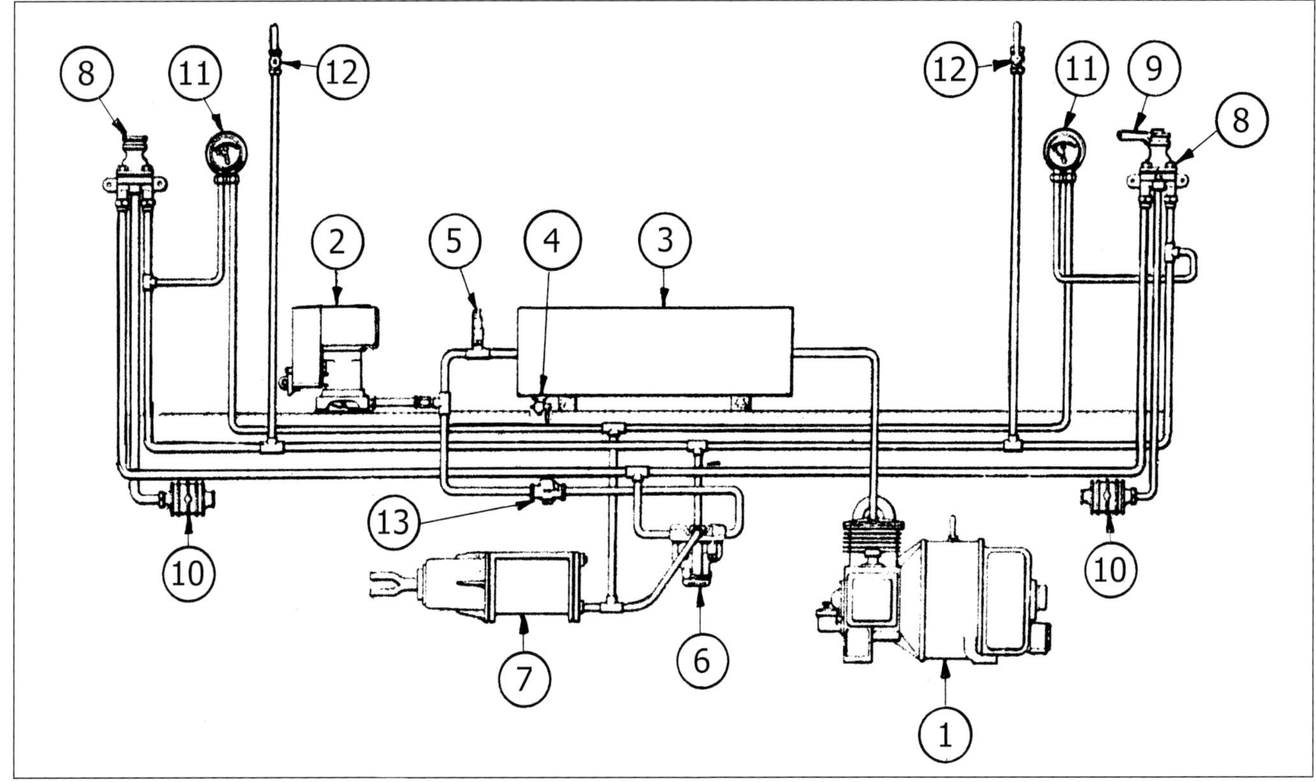

Diagram 39. Schedule of main components

1 Compressor
2 Compressor governor
3 Main reservoir
4 Drain cock – main reservoir
5 Safety valve
6 Emergency valve
7 Brake cylinder
8 Driver's brake valve
9 Brake valve operating handle
10 Brake valve exhaust silencer
11 Duplex pressure gauge
12 Conductor's emergency valve
13 Strainer for emergency valve

How the air brake system works

To energise the system the compressor 1 is switched on. This switch, which is located on one of the driving platforms, may be either a 'knife' or 'rotary' type with a fuse fitted in the same unit. As the switch operates at line voltage and can be delicate, care must be taken when switching off when the compressor is working; this can only be recommended in an emergency. The switch should be turned off, off load, when the compressor governor 2 has switched off (i.e. cuts out) the motor driving the compressor. It is not good practice to remove the trolley from the wire with the compressor working. This will create an arc that may burn the wire and trolley wheel or carbon skid. The time between the compressor governor 2 cutting out and the pressure dropping so much that the switch re-closes, should provide ample time to turn the trolley.

When problems arise during the turning of the trolley (e.g. the swivel head has got itself at a right angle to the wire) it may be advisable to switch off the compressor. This will avoid the pump being subjected to a series of bursts of power while repeated attempts are made to put the trolley back on the wire! As there is no starting resistor to cushion this motor, repeated bursts of power will shorten its life. Always remember to switch the compressor back on again afterwards.

The compressor system should be switched off and the hand-brake fully applied when the tramcar is left unattended.

Air is drawn in and compressed by the electrically-driven compressor 1. The pressure of the air is controlled by the compressor governor 2, which switches the compressor motor on when the air pressure is low, and off when the required pressure has been achieved.

The compressed air is stored in a tank called the main reservoir 3. (Note, there may be more than one reservoir fitted, depending on the design of the air system and the space available).

To release air from the system and remove any quantity of condensation accumulated in the system, a drain valve 4 is mounted in the lowest point of the reservoir.

If there is a problem with the compressor governor and the air is compressed to a high pressure that could cause damage to air system components, the safety valve 5 will release the air pressure.

In the event of an emergency brake application by the driver's brake valve 8 or conductors emergency valve 12, the emergency valve will release air from the main reservoir 3 to the brake cylinder 7, applying the brakes with the maximum force available.

The brake cylinder 7 is connected to the brake rigging, enabling the brake shoes to be applied to the wheels or track, dependent on the type of brakes fitted.

The driver's brake valve 8, sometimes referred to as the motorman's valve controls the air pressure to the brake cylinder 7.

The driver's brake valve 8 is operated by the insertion of a handle 9, which is transferred from end to end.

When air is released from the brake cylinder 7 via the driver's brake valve 8, it is passed through the exhaust silencer 10 to reduce the noise.

Air pressure in the main reservoir 3 and the brake cylinder 7 are monitored by the duplex pressure gauge 11. Usually the red finger on the gauge indicates reservoir pressure and the black finger brake cylinder pressure (note some systems have separate gauges for reservoir and brake pressures and may have a third gauge to indicate track brake pressure if fitted).

In an emergency, the conductor can apply the brakes

using the valve 12, which operates the emergency valve 6 as described above.

To prevent dirt entering the emergency valve 6 a strainer valve 13 is fitted in the pipeline.

Operation of a straight air brake valve employing 'poppet' valves

There are three positions for the handle: one to release the brake pressure, one lap/running, and one for application of the brake pressure. Note: there is no emergency application position, as a separate 'conductor's' emergency valve is usually located adjacent to the driver's controls.

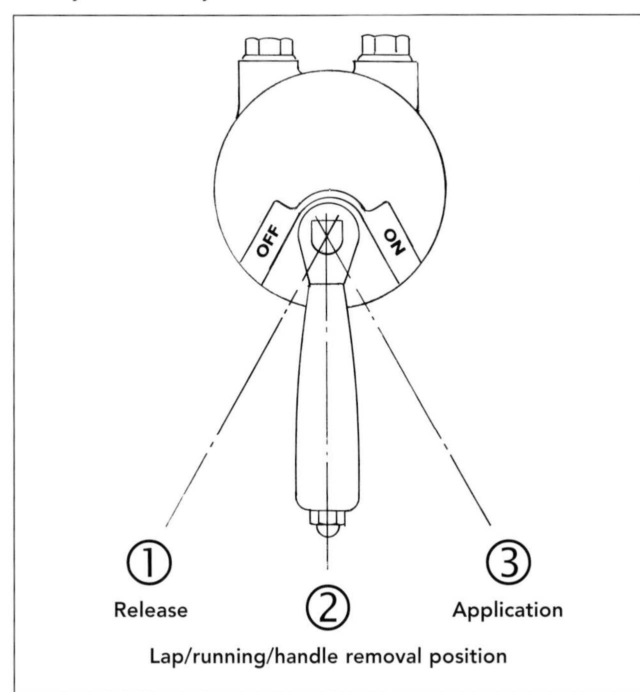

Diagram 40

① Release

Moving the handle to the left from the mid lap/running/handle removal position will release air pressure from the brake cylinder. The handle has to be held in the release position to overcome the spring force in the 'poppet' valve, releasing force on the handle will return to the mid lap/running/handle removal position.

② Lap/Running/Handle Removal Position

All valve ports are closed; brake is not applied or released and is the position the handle is to be kept when the tramcar is in motion.
N.B. The handle can only be removed or inserted in this position.

③ Application

Moving the handle to the right from the mid lap/running/handle removal position will apply air pressure to the brake cylinder. The handle has to be held in the application position to overcome the spring force in the 'poppet' valve, releasing force on the handle will return to the mid lap/running/handle removal position.

Graduation of the brake force

When making a service brake application the driver may find that the tramcar is stopping short of the intended point owing to too much air having been admitted to the brake cylinder. By moving the handle to the release position for a short period and then back to "lap", air will be released from the brake cylinder – so reducing the brake force.
Should the tramcar not be stopping at the intended point, the driver will move the handle towards the service application position for a short period and then back to "lap". This action will allow more air into the brake cylinder. By these simple actions, the driver can graduate the brake force very easily and make perfectly smooth stops without causing the wheels to skid.

The amount of pressure in the brake cylinder can be easily monitored on the brake pressure gauge.

Self-lapping Driver's Brake Valve

There can be four positions on the self-lapping brake valve: one to fully release the brake force, one to apply full service braking, one to remove handle, and one for an emergency application.

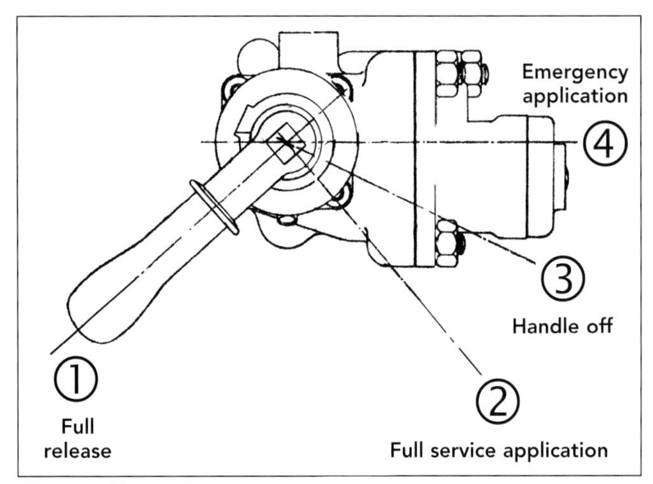

Diagram 41

① Full Release

Handle to extreme left position, air is released from the brake cylinder including that applied by emergency application position on the brake valve or conductor's emergency valve.

This is also the run/lap position of the handle when the tramcar is in motion and no brake control actions are to be taken.

② Full Service Application

The full service position is obtained by moving the handle through 90 degrees to the right of the full release position. By moving the handle to the right, from the full release position, the brakes are applied by building up pressure in the brake cylinder to a value that corresponds to the degree of movement of the handle.

Moving the handle to the left from any position between full service and full release will give an immediate and corresponding reduction in brake cylinder pressure.

③ Handle Off

A position mid way between full service and emergency application is the only location the handle can be removed from the valve. The brake cylinder pressure is maintained automatically when the driver removes the brake handle to go to the other end of the tramcar.

④ Emergency application

For an emergency application of the air brake, the driver moves the handle to the extreme right position, leaving it there. This will allow air from the reservoir to enter the brake cylinder at a force higher than the full service application, instantly, via the emergency valve.
N.B. Application of the emergency brake may vent all other pipes – dependent on arrangement of pipe connections – to atmosphere including the pressure gauges, which will read zero air pressure when in fact the brake pressure is at maximum.

Releasing the Emergency Brake Application

To release the emergency brake application the handle is moved to the full release position. If the air is not released, move the handle back to the emergency position, then wait for the compressor to fully charge the system before retrying the full release position.

Straight Air Brake Valve

This is the simplest form of Air-brake valve (diagram 42), but with none of the refinements of the other types, it needs much skill from the driver to operate it successfully. The motorman's valve handle can only be removed in the lap (i.e. neutral) position. Care must be exercised that this is done accurately, otherwise operation of the valve at the other platform will be compromised.

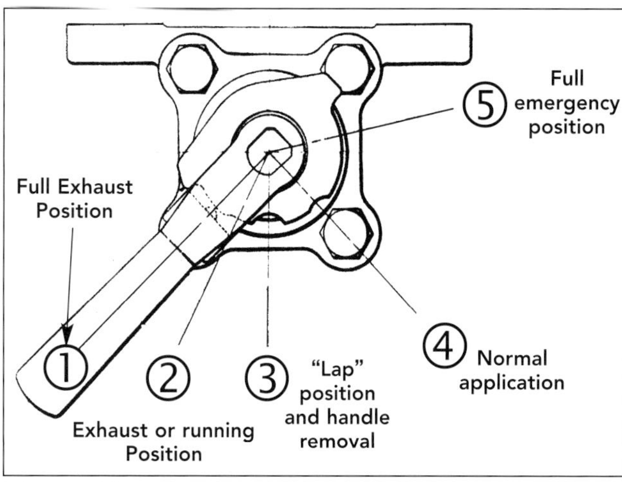

Diagram 42

Never leave the tramcar parked on the emergency air brake. Transfer to the parking brake as soon as possible after bringing the tramcar to rest.

4.3 Operating the Tramway and its Equipment

The point-iron is a driver's tool for changing points. When conductors (or others) are entrusted with this task, they should be encouraged always to stand facing the tram, never with their back to it. Even if the tram has stopped, an inadvertent move on the driver's part could cause the tram to set in motion. Anyone not facing the tramcar may not get out of the way quickly enough.

When operating points always listen out for the "clump" sound that should indicate that the point toggle mechanism has travelled over centre, and the springs are holding the blade in the new position. When operating pull-cord frogs (points in the overhead line system) make sure that the correct cord has been pulled, and if possible look up and see that the movable blade has travelled far enough.

Points are the tram driver's most dangerous item of track-work, presenting the driver with a number of hazards. When nearing any facing points (i.e. those approached from where the point-blades are) drivers must carefully check that the blades are fully home. Speed must be no more than 5mph (8kph). Drivers must beware of debris fouling or blocking the point-blades or crossings.

Don't reverse over point-work – drivers must always ensure that their tram is well clear of points before reversing. Only if there is no alternative may drivers reverse direction over point-work, and then only after each point-blade has been moved to the position corresponding to the direction from which the tram will arrive over the points.

Sprung points should not be taken for granted – springs can fail or become jammed, so drivers should always approach them with caution. Remember too that trolley equipped cars often have points to negotiate (called frogs) in the overhead wiring. Not all frogs can be trailed through without being first set in the proper position.

When using points to enter a siding off the "main-line", remember that drivers must ensure that the points are returned to the main-line position after their car has cleared such point-work. The only exception to this rule is when the siding is a trailing connection to a track used in one direction only.

At junctions where the track configuration could lead to

Tram driver's cockpit 1935 style – Darwen Corp. Tramways 23. Similar but narrower than the Blackpool Streamliners, these two cars were later sold (1946) to the Llandudno & Colwyn Bay Electric Railway Company. Despite the expense of re-gauging – from Darwen's 4 feet to the Welsh tramway's 3ft 6in., they were banned by the Ministry of Transport from carrying passengers over the Little Orme section, and could only be employed on short workings at each end of the line. Note the sliding door fitted to the bulkhead, and lack of a driver's seat.
Jim Halsall collection – Photographer Unknown

a collision if passing tramcars derailed or point blades moved suddenly, most operators insist on a prohibition of trams passing one another. E.g. at facing crossovers, or right-hand double-track junctions, the second car must stop and wait until the first tram has cleared the points and crossings. Three good reasons support this rule:

1 Point blades could move under passing trams.
2 One driver may have mis-read the setting of the points.
3 An obstruction in the crossing castings could lead to a derailment – bad enough in itself, but potentially catastrophic when a head-on crash results.

This no passing rule does not apply on railway type point-work when points are detected and locked in their final position, and point position indicators (signals) verify the integrity of the selected route. Railway-type track-work laid on sleepers does not have the same supporting surface as paved tramway point-work, and will therefore not allow a derailed tram to travel far outside its normal swept path.

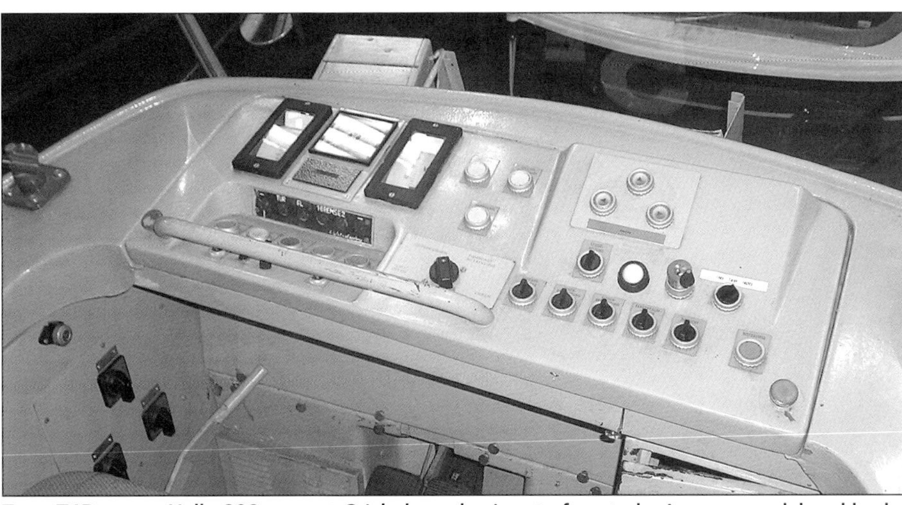

Tatra T4D car ex-Halle 902, now at Crich, has a basic set of controls. A power pedal and brake pedal are the basic means of controlling the car. Left to right on the console are traction ammeter, tacho (speedometer), battery voltage; in the centre are push buttons for the holding brake, a button for the wash-plant, and the lowest button is for the warning signal (doors). Other buttons and switches operate lighting, doors, heating, and trafficators.

A 1928 interurban tram (Schöneiche 35) with its built-in kitchen arrangement. Perhaps this was the contemporary mode! Right of the controller at the back is the trafficator switch, with the sand operating lever alongside. At the front is the air-brake valve (with handle removed), and handbrake. To the extreme right can be seen the air-pressure gauges.

Finally, drivers must not allow trams to run over stones or debris, even on plain track. This applies especially to metal objects such as engineers' nuts or bolts lying in the tram rail groove, which can cause derailments.

4.3 The Tramway and its Overhead Line Equipment

Procedure at Termini

At termini it is the driver's sole responsibility to ensure that the current collector is correctly turned – and in the case of trolleys placed on the appropriate wire – even if this task is delegated. Trolley ropes should be correctly stowed after use, and when in use never ever wrapped around a person's fingers or hand. Where trolley canes (bamboo poles) are used these must be handled with care. Never place these on the ground and take great care when removing/returning them from/to the tram side mounting. Do not scratch adjacent paint-work and ensure the cane is mounted correctly in its fitting. When inserting the hook at the end of the cane to lower the trolley do not use the safety rope, but place the hook around the trolley boom. Never move a tram with a trolley cane attached.

Special procedures must apply when open-topped trams carrying passengers have their trolleys turned. A staff member must be in position at the stair-head to supervise that top-deck passengers remain seated while their colleague turns the trolley. Open topped trams must not use automatic trolley reversers (see below) – especially when passengers are on board.

When a tram is equipped with two trolleys it is good practice to raise the "new" trolley before lowering the one previously in use. This will allow continuity of supply to lighting etc. A change-over switch is usually provided to prevent the lowered trolley still remaining "live".

Automatic trolley reversers were a feature found only on tramway systems using trams fitted with trolley poles without ropes attached.

Taking the form of a triangle of overhead wiring, the equipment provided a reversing facility for trolley poles. Fitted at termini and frequently used crossovers drivers would first stop their tram just beyond a spring-biased frog. After changing ends the driver would reverse the tramcar

The tram driver's cockpit designed for Nottingham in 2002.

A point-cleaner at work in Sheffield near Fitzalan Square in 1958. Car 189 waits to pass in the days long before "Hi-Vis" warning vests were invented. Since 1992 trams once again traverse this location East of Castle Square

slowly as the trolley (still at the same end of the car) would be pushed through the triangle as far as the apex of the triangle. A second sprung frog would allow the passage of the trolley-head into the final length of trolley wire. At this point the trolley is roughly at 90 degrees to the tram, and at its maximum reach. As the tram continues its path the trolley changes its direction and follows the tram to the rear of the vehicle. The operation is now complete, and not only do the tram-crew not have to do this manually, but the car lighting can remain illuminated – an important safety feature. Although primarily designed for swivel head trolleys, a reverser used by fixed head trolleys existed for some years at Blackpool North Station terminus.

Trolley retriever is the generic name for a device that either catches (trolley catcher) or retrieves (trolley retriever) a trolley pole in the event of a dewirement. A trolley catcher catches and holds the trolley rope, leaving the trolley head just above the height of the trolley wire. A trolley retriever, in the event of a dewirement, catches the trolley rope and by means of a powerful spring draws it down to prevent damage to overhead line fittings. These devices are usually fitted to the dash panels of trams – a bayonet fitting being employed for easy removal when the trolley needs turning on cars not fitted with two poles. It is imperative that only members of staff trained in the use of these devices are allowed to do so. Both types have stored spring energy that

Leeds 399 at the National Tramway Museum uses the automatic trolley reverser at Town End terminus on 1 April, 2006.

can easily be triggered by misuse and cause serious personal injury. It is common practice in North America – where the use of these devices is widespread – to issue staff with work gloves for use when operating them. Some operators who used tramcars fitted with pantographs employed these devices to gather up the slack on the ropes used for lowering pantographs. Modern light rail vehicles have pantographs equipped with pneumatic or electric/stored spring mechanisms that can lower or raise the pantographs at the flick of a switch.

Car lighting (interior lights) and car lights (head/tail lights) will go out during the trolley turning operation (except when using a trolley reverser, see above). When lighting is in use passengers on the tram should be warned in advance of this short blackout. Drivers should ensure that when reversing a tram its head and tail-lights are changed in accordance with the new direction. Any platform lights should be unlit at the driver's end, and night-blinds put in place to prevent car interior lighting causing reflections on the driver's windscreen.

A tower wagon is an essential piece of equipment on any tramway system. This car was "home-made" by Leeds City Tramways using components from scrapped trams. Visible in the top right hand of the photo can be seen a "drop lever frog" in the overhead wiring. In this photo all types of current collector can be seen. Left is newly arrived Halle 902 with a diamond framed pantograph. In the centre the bow collector of Tower 2, while at the right is shown its trolley pole.

CHAPTER 5

Abnormal Incidents

Tramways have a good safety record, and well organised tramway operators not only do their utmost to maintain this, but prepare their staff to cope with any eventuality by training programmes that rehearse and simulate various forms of crisis. The golden rule is that tramway staff should always act in a calm and professional manner. Above all they must feel confident to provide a lead, taking charge where necessary, and promoting the safety of passengers who will expect staff to provide guidance with authority. With heritage tramcars, even the loud bang and flash of a circuit breaker opening under a heavy load can distress some passengers. When this happens a few words of re-assurance that the equipment is functioning as designed may restore calm. Similarly, smoke emanating from a controller after a flash-over could cause panic. Normally, this will extinguish itself. If the Fire Brigade are called to an incident they will take charge on arrival, but tram-crew must stay at the scene to assist in any technical matter as required.

Drivers must always make their first action that of making the tram safe: i.e. hand-brake fully applied, controller key removed, main circuit-breaker (and battery isolation switch, if fitted) switched off. This must be done before leaving the platform to respond to any incident. After dark, staff must evacuate passengers before switching off lighting.

Staff should never make comments to passengers about an incident or its possible causes. A few ill-chosen words may inspire a claim for damages in this litigious age. Unless it is essential to do so for reasons of personal rescue or safety, no measures must be taken that could remove or destroy evidence.

5.1 Fire

Whenever a fire is reported or suspected drivers must stop their tram immediately. The handbrake is to be applied and, during daytime, the current collector removed from the wire and tied down. During hours of darkness and in the case of trams not fitted with emergency (i.e. battery-fed) lighting, the evacuation of passengers must take priority; therefore, car lighting must be kept on if possible. But all circuits other than lighting should be switched off at the appropriate circuit breakers or switches. Once all passengers have disembarked the current collector should be lowered and tied down. Passengers should be encouraged to use all available exits, but staff should not omit to warn of the danger of passing traffic on street sections. On sleeper track it may be more dangerous to evacuate passengers, particularly where uneven ground is encountered. Unless there is a fire hazard, it may be better to keep the passengers on board until a replacement car arrives. This is certainly the case during electrical storms. The tramcar provides a virtual "Faraday cage", so even if lightning strikes the tram, no physical harm should occur to passengers.

If the source of a fire can be removed from the tram (e.g. a smouldering seat squab) do this if it is safe to do so. If the fire can be fought with the extinguisher provided, this should be done if there is no risk to personal safety. When doing so always ensure that your own exit path is clear. Sand and dry earth can be used to cut off oxygen to the fire. Help should be summoned without delay, but keep all passengers well clear, and warn them not to attempt to re-board the tram.

Once the fire has been extinguished, the current collector must NOT be put back on the wire. The stricken vehicle must be slowly towed back to the depot yard for full technical examination – (beware of strong air currents re-igniting any smouldering material).

5.2 Loss of Power Supply

In the event of the sudden loss of power, the driver must stop and investigate. First the handbrake must be applied, and then the controller key removed. The following checks should then be made:

a Is the current collector still in contact with the trolley wire?

b Has the tram become "grounded"? (See section 5.3 below for a full explanation.)

Fire on roof of Nuremberg tram, August 1982

If "a" can be answered "yes", and "b" with "no", one set of car lights should then be switched on. The lights will be lit when the power is restored. Beware: the absence of traction voltage car lighting must never be taken as a safe guarantee that the current is off; it could be that a bulb has failed! Once electricity has returned, drivers must only use the 'Series' notches of power until advised otherwise by the supervising officer – to whom a verbal report of the temporary loss of power must be made.

If other trams in the same feeder section are receiving power it can be assumed that the fault is on the driver's allocated tram. A safety fuse box is fitted to many heritage tramcars close to the current collector. This contains a modern fuse rated above the setting of the circuit breakers, and which if "blown" will remove all the 600-volt electrical supply. Further investigation should reveal if the problem concerns the current collector. Is it on a dead section of overhead? Has the trolley wire been encircled with ice? If the latter applies, then careful use of a bamboo pole may detach the ice. N.B. If you are the driver of a stranded tram needing to be pushed away from a dead section, always ensure that your tram's controller is switched off before any movement takes place.

5.3 Grounding

In the event of a tram becoming isolated from the earth return provided by the rails (i.e. in tramway parlance: grounded), the correct procedure must be followed. Be aware that the tram's chassis and all attached metal handrails are likely to be electrically live at 600 volts above earth! Having applied the handbrake the next priority is to prevent anyone attempting to board or alight (or even touch the tram!). Next switch off all circuits (including the compressor where fitted). Then, carefully jump off the tram's step, being conscious of the need not to form an electrical bridge to earth with your own body! Finally, remove the current collector and tie it down. Only now is it safe to evacuate the passengers. The use of a (dry) wooden-handled brush can remove excessive sand from the rails; and following that, a bucket full of water poured into the rail groove on higher ground than where the tram stands, can restore conductivity. Gravity will convey it to where it is needed.

5.4 Electric Shock

Do not touch the victim. Try and isolate the electrical supply if a switch is nearby. If this cannot be done you may attempt to separate the victim from the supply by tugging on his/her dry clothing. If on board a tram, make the tram safe, remove the current collector from the wire and tie it down, then assist the victim. Electric shock involving direct current often results in severe burns, but cardiac problems can arise. First Aid and medical assistance must be summoned as soon as possible, and the victim made as comfortable as possible, without moving him/her. Under no circumstances should the person be left unaccompanied.

5.5 De-wirements and Overhead Line Failure

A de-wirement is the name given to the mishap when the trolley-pole unexpectedly leaves the overhead wire. This is something that happens most frequently in a depot yard where diverging wires and frogs provide almost a natural hazard. In this kind of location speeds are low, and the conductor should be closely monitoring the progress of the trolley, ready to give an acoustic emergency stop signal.

A de-wirement on plain track inevitably involves a higher speed, and this means a strong possibility that damage has been inflicted on the trolley pole or its head, or overhead wiring/fittings. Drivers must always immediately report such an incident happening away from the depot yard. A technical inspection must be carried out to determine if damage has been caused.

Trolley catchers and trolley retrievers were widely used in the USA to automatically lower the trolley pole at speed when a de-wirement happened. (See Section 4.1 for more details.)

Whilst bow collectors and pantographs seldom leave the overhead in the way described above, when things do go wrong the result is very dramatic. A Leeds tram once lost its pantograph in a snagging incident, and parts were later discovered on the roof of a nearby cinema! Slack converging wires are the most common cause of snagging problems. Whilst the bow collector will lower itself if snagged, and possibly free itself, this is not so with a pantograph. A slack converging wire, instead of running on to the horns of the pantograph head may well go underneath and rip the head apart.

Overhead Line Failure

It is sometimes said that a good tram driver needs three eyes: One to monitor the track, one to watch the overhead, and a third to scan the space between the two! Not only is the overhead line and its equipment full of potentially

Oporto 273 at Crich depot with a trolley catcher mounted above the headlight.

The first accident witnessed by the author in Aachen in 1968. The motorist had omitted to look right and was hit by the gutter-running tram heading towards the camera on what tramway-men call: running "bang-road".

dangerous electricity, it is also under considerable mechanical tension. The whiplash from broken wires can cause serious injury. Alert drivers can prevent a small failure leading to a catastrophic failure. The passage of a trolley pole or pantograph under defective wiring is potentially dangerous. It should only be attempted at very low speed under the close supervision of an overhead line technician.

Where failure has caused wiring literally to fall out of the sky, this is to be treated as an emergency by any staff discovering this. Telephone or radio must be used immediately to switch off the power supply to the section affected. The fallen wiring should be cordoned off to prevent the unwary getting close to it – remember also that the mechanical tension remains a source of danger.

Derailments

When a tram is separated from its rails the return current path is interrupted and consequently it should be assumed that a grounding has resulted. The procedure outlined in Section 5.2 must be carried out. Only then is it safe for the passengers to disembark. Engineering assistance must be summoned before the commencement of any attempts to re-rail the tram.

5.6 Collision with another tramcar

Heritage trams are usually well engineered to withstand low speed shunts, and the need to closely park trams in depots can lead to many a low speed 'kiss'. The situation is much more serious when the accident occurs with passengers aboard – especially at stops where the unloading process has begun, and people may be knocked off balance. The welfare of passengers must be the priority of staff in this situation. Evidence must be preserved and recorded, e.g. was sand applied, and for how long? The names and addresses of witnesses should be taken down and an incident report prepared (see below).

Many collisions are the result of drivers not assessing speed or braking performance correctly. Best practice when pulling up close to another vehicle is first to stop short, then draw up slowly with a partially applied hand-brake.

5.7 Road Traffic Accidents

Accidents can happen even in the best-regulated organisations. Not every motorist is aware that trams cannot be steered clear of obstructions. Some seem to think that the trams are no wider than the tracks they run on! Unless injury

The author only visited Aachen twice (i.e. during 1968/9) but each time he was there one of the trams he rode on had a traffic accident! Both incidents were more costly for the motorist – the trams were not scratched.

to persons has happened, or one party has violated traffic regulations, there is no requirement to call the police. Good reporting of facts and details of witnesses are essential, as is the exchange of insurers' details.

See Section 5.9 below for full procedures regarding incident reporting.

5.8 Dealing with Passengers and Customers with Mobility Problems

Mobility Impairment Awareness

5.8.1

Passengers who use a wheelchair are individuals in their own right. They are people whose feelings, sense of awareness, needs, and dignity are as valid as any other person's. They have every right to expect all members of staff to exercise a duty of care towards others, and to be treated with respect and consideration.

5.8.2

The fact that an individual is mobility impaired does in itself not mean that the person in a wheelchair is mentally ill-equipped. Staff should always first try and communicate with the person in the wheelchair, rather than ignore them and go to the companion in the classic "Does he take sugar?" approach.

5.8.3

Staff should at all times show respect and be sensitive towards the mobility impaired (M.I) visitors':

- Right to exercise choice at all times.
- Fear of being not in control of one's person.
- Feeling of being surrounded by able-bodied giants.
- Feeling of exclusion in a world designed for the able-bodied.

5.8.4

Staff should be alert to the danger of appearing to be condescending. M.I. Visitors need empathy rather than sympathy. When talking to M.I. visitors staff need to adopt a friendly and relaxed attitude, avoiding "talking down" to wheelchair users. Wherever possible staff should sit, squat, or bend, so that eye-contact is made at an acceptably equal level.

5.8.5
Always ask permission from the wheelchair user before making any move or adjustment to the wheelchair. Explain, in an unhurried way the proposed move or action, and getting permission to do so, will promote the mobility impaired visitor's feeling of being in safe and respectful hands.

5.8.6
Passengers affected by communications difficulties may sometimes be helped by careful prompts. The use of questions that can be answered by a simple "yes" or "no" is recommended. Staff should have notepaper and pen handy for those who can only communicate by writing or sketching. It will assist visitors who can lip-read if staff always face the person to whom they are speaking, and do not cover their own mouth.

5.8.7
Members of staff should be aware that people in wheelchairs almost always feel cold out of doors, and need protection against prolonged exposure to windy and draughty places.

5.8.8 Wheelchair Handling
Some wheelchair users may have certain illnesses or conditions that make them vulnerable to serious complications. These may develop following seemingly minor abrasions or bruising. One example is diabetes. A case at a Sheffield hospital ten years ago involved a seemingly trivial bruise to a patient whose wheelchair was being moved by a member of the Occupational Therapy Department. The bruising resisted all attempts at treatment, complications arose, and the final outcome was that the patient's leg had to be amputated.

When negotiating tight clearances members of staff should ensure that the limbs of the wheelchair user are kept within the extremities of the chair itself. Never move a wheelchair unless the leg- and foot-rests are in their correct positions.

Look for the brakes on the wheelchair, seek confirmation on how they are applied, and remember that both brakes to the major wheels need to be applied to prevent movement.

Where a slope or step needs to be traversed, always approach it so that if the wheelchair has to be tipped in any way this is done by pulling from behind the seat, and not endangering the Mobility Impaired visitor by any risk of over-balancing. If in doubt seek assistance.

Many designs of wheelchair have detachable armrests and sides. Before attempting to assist any movement ensure that the part of the wheelchair you may think to get hold of, will not – when grasped – come away in your hands!

5.8.9
It is NOT recommended practice to attempt to lift visitors from their wheelchairs. Staff, if asked for assistance by a visitor wishing to transfer from their chair to a tramcar seat, should offer a steadying hand only, and clearly state this in advance. Lifting an adult person can damage you as well as the visitor. If a visitor insists on making the transfer, always check that they have applied both brakes on their wheelchair before they lift themselves out of it.

N.B. Wheelchairs should always be parked on board a tram with BOTH brakes applied.

Dealing with Customers
Whenever they are approached by a customer, staff should bear in mind that they represent the human face of the operating organisation. Politeness and courtesy are the qualities expected of staff. Even when unable to answer a particular enquiry he/she should offer to take the visitor to someone who may well know, or by use of radio or telephone contact a person in higher authority.

The average heritage tramway depends solely on continuing to attract visitors in sufficient numbers to keep the operation viable. The visitor has paid for a pleasant experience, but if this expectation is not fulfilled, not only will he/she not return, but very likely the negative assessment will be shared among family, friends, and work colleagues.

5.9 The Reporting of Incidents
The sequel to incidents described in this chapter must include the accurate reporting of such mishaps. The definition of an incident includes an event which has involved actual or potential (i.e. a near miss) injury to any person, or damage to any property, or for any infringement of rules, regulations, or bylaws.

The reporting of an incident is the start of a process that can have wide-reaching consequences, usually by completing a pro-forma incident/accident report document. By the use of a numbering system and registering the issue of each form, a careful check can be made, and the person to whom the form was first issued can be sought out if there is a delay in the form being completed and returned. Some organisations insist on such forms being completed and handed in before the end of the shift.

All members of staff named in

To enable visitors in wheelchairs to enjoy a tram ride at the National Tramway Museum, Berlin 3006 was acquired and converted for this purpose in 1996. A wheelchair lift enables passengers to board easily.

such a report should be given the opportunity to comment. Names of witnesses should be recorded, along with their contact details.

All salient details are to be documented; and if a mobile camera phone, or camera, is available a photographic record should be made. All these details should be included:

- Location.
- Date.
- Time.
- Weather conditions.
- Rail condition.
- Vehicle details.
- Vehicle speed.
- Vehicle lights in use.
- Estimated measurements of positions of all relevant participants.
- Any other relevant information.

There are a variety of reasons why incident reports are necessary:

- The insurers require such notification.
- Legislation demands it (see The Railway Safety Directive 2004/49/EC, or the Railways and Transport Safety Act 2003, and The Railways [Accident Investigation and Reporting] Regulations 2005).
- Reporting of Injuries, Diseases, and Dangerous Occurrences, Regulations. 1995 (A.K.A: RIDDOR 95).
- Feedback.

Incidents and accidents, when adequately and correctly recorded, and properly investigated can be valuable sources of learning. Well established facts through good feedback can highlight areas where safety can be enhanced and perhaps procedures may be amended. The records of incidents can provide the basis of a comprehensive resource of operating experience.

It is therefore imperative that incidents are reported concerning dewirements outside the depot area, or any derailment on any track, or any major equipment failure (especially involving safety critical equipment). Furthermore, human failings are to be reported:

- Breach of safety regulations.
- Breach of operating procedures.
- Any shunt (however minor).
- Any near miss (i.e. a dangerous occurrence that could have led to an accident).
- Any untoward event of a safety nature that could be the cause of comment from a passenger, or the media, should be reported.
- Accident at a level crossing with a road.
- Pedestrian fatality, or accident causing a life threatening injury.
- Any fall from a doorway when tram is in motion.
- Any incident causing an interruption in service for more than an hour.
- Line blockage caused by unsafe scaffolding, or structural failure of a civil engineering nature.
- A runaway tram, (railed) trailer, or engineers' trolley.

In addition to a full incident report, advice should be sought from the Officer-in-Charge (and where equipment failure is suspected, the Engineer-in-Charge) on the appropriate action or remedy following the incident.

Where malfunction of equipment is suspected, engineering support and advice must be sought, and a defect report completed (in addition to the completion of the incident report).

In the event of a serious mishap taking place, no action must be taken – with the exception of measures necessary for rescue or the saving of life – which might result in valuable evidence being destroyed or lost.

In the case of minor incidents, members of staff should not be deflected from recording and reporting the incident. Members of the public may well say that they "don't want to make a fuss", but later change their minds. An apparently minor injury may become the tip of the iceberg, resulting in a claim for damages at a later date. If a member of the public makes an allegation of a slip or fall on a vehicle or on company property, this too should be recorded. Do this, even if you were not a witness to the alleged incident. If a claim is made at a later date and no recorded information can be found, this may have expensive consequences to the operating organisation, especially in the event of a greatly exaggerated claim being made.

Staff should be guarded in what they say, and never make self-opinionated statements regarding the cause of an incident to any unauthorised person. Your rash or unguarded comments may be used in evidence against the operating organisation by members of the public who are well aware of the present day potential for litigation and substantial claims for compensation.

Members of staff should never make any comments or give statements to the press or media, unless they have been authorised to do so by the management.

A driver's eye view of the York Road reserved track tramway in Leeds in May 1958

CHAPTER 6

Signing in at the Start of a Shift and Leaving the Depot

6.1 Pre-service Checks

The driver's duty should commence on the day before he/she signs in at the start of the shift! For example, taking notice of the weather forecast is an important preparation. It could determine the choice of uniform clothing which will be required, e.g. a forecast of cold weather can prompt us to get out the mittens and a heavy overcoat; warnings of fog can be a prompt to re-read the Rule Book concerning procedures to be followed in foggy conditions.

As well as being smartly turned out in uniform complete with cap, a driver will need to carry the following:

- Tram driving licence (this may be in the form of an identity-card with photo, entitling the bearer to carry out safety critical work).
- Watch/timepiece.
- Pen.
- Whistle.
- Clean cloth to wipe windscreens.
- Rule Book (emergency contact telephone numbers to be printed in this document, or on the running board issued to the driver – see below).

At the signing-on location, careful perusal of the notice board for warning notices, restrictions, and points of information should be carried out by all crew. The act of signing in is a legally binding statement affirming that the driver and conductor considers him/herself fit for duty with respect to the consumption of drugs and alcohol.

Some operators hold a briefing meeting at which the Line Manager (title may vary e.g. Supervisor, Inspector, etc.) will communicate verbally with drivers and conductors and impart items of information.

The driver will be issued with the relevant paper-work, which may include:

- A "Running board", the timetable for the duty, which will give arrival and departure times for specific locations; and list times for meal breaks.
- A pre-service check-list, which must be signed by the driver on completion of the checks. The condition of the tram being the responsibility of the driver, as it is with LGV and PCV drivers, and their vehicles.
- A document for reporting defects concerning the tram.
- Incident/accident report form.
- An Operating Manual for the specific tram type.

Equipment for use during the shift will be handed out at this time including emergency equipment e.g., torches for night-time use.

Two factors now need careful scrutiny:

a That the allocated tram is within the appropriate class-qualification of the assigned driver.

b The other is that the chosen tram has been designated serviceable by the relevant engineering department. The latter can be verified by reference to a fleet serviceability list (and can be double-checked by inspecting the "Tramcars Stopped" board).

The chosen tram must appear on the "Serviceable" Board – along with today's date and a valid signature, and most definitely not appear on the "Tramcars Stopped" list.

Only at this stage does the driver get close to the chosen tram and can start the pre-service checks.

Assuming that the tram is at the front of the depot track, the checks can commence as the tram is approached:

6.1.1 The Exterior Features

The driver should first walk around the tram:

- Ensuring that no one is working on or near to this vehicle.
- All doors are unlocked and available for use.
- There are no "Stop Boards" or "Do Not Move" notices on the tram.
- Check the rail conditions e.g. excessive sand or dirt on the rail top may cause a "grounding" problem, see section 5.1.3 for advice.
- The car is free to move (with no chocks or obstructions near to the wheels), and that the rails ahead are free from piles of sand dropped by other trams. No-one has coupled the tram to the one behind using the coupling pin retainers (it is very embarrassing leaving the depot with two trams!).
- Accident damage: e.g., broken windows, damaged paint-work, or any loose fittings.
- No wires/cables or any other items are loose or dangling from the underside of the tram.
- Track brakes are set at the correct level above the rail head.
- The tram's brake shoes are in correct relationship with wheels.
- No obstructions in the depot will prevent leaving, e.g. equipment left lying around. Check that depot doors are fully opened.
- Check that the overhead line is live (it is common practice to have indicator lights showing that the overhead is switched on).
- The cleanliness of the tram, with particular reference to windscreens, platform vestibule glazing, mirrors, head and tail lights. If the tram is considered to be too dirty it should be reported as defective to the Supervisor.

6.1.2 Current Collector Trolley Pole Installation

- The trolley head is in alignment with overhead wire (not twisted).
- Safety rope (i.e. device between trolley head and pole) is in place and in good condition.
- Insulation on trolley pole is not damaged. This is important on open top tramcars as it could lead to electric shock if the exposed metal of the pole comes in contact with a live overhead fitting, thus making the pole live at 600 volts.
- The trolley rope is secured to pole and in good condition (a gentle pull on the rope is advised). Care should been taken if the rope is saturated with water and fixed to a live pole (pole without insulation) as it can give an electric shock. Any knots or loops other than at the end of the rope must be removed as these can lead to a dewirement if caught in a body fixture or fitting.
- Any trolley cane carried is in good condition with no splits, and its hook is secure. It is important that the cane is dry and clean, a damp and/or dirty cane can lead to an electric shock if contact is made with any live part of the trolley or overhead line.

N.B. If the trolley cane is stored under the tram or adjacent to its wheels, it can become coated in iron brake dust that will conduct electricity!

If a trolley cane that is located at an overhead line support mast is to be used, the same care should be taken to inspect for damage and damp.

Never lay a trolley cane on the ground as it can easily be damaged.

The trolley rope or a trolley cane is the means to remove the collector from the overhead line and isolate the tram from the power supply. A broken or damaged trolley rope should be repaired as a matter of urgency and a trolley cane must be carried at all times when a trolley rope is not fitted.

See section 4.2. paragraph 3 for instructions on how to use a trolley cane.

Bow Collector

- Check that the bow collector is the correct way round for the direction of travel. Depending on the overhead line installation, it may be possible to travel a short distance with the bow in the leading direction of travel without it turning over. Do not push the bow in this way through any frogs or special work in the overhead wiring. If in doubt, seek instructions from the supervisor.
- Check that the bow is at right angles to the overhead wire, and is not damaged or twisted.
- Check that the bow ropes are secured to bow collector, and in good condition (a gentle pull on each of the ropes is advised). Care should been taken if the rope is saturated with water, as the ropes are usually secured to the bow structure which is live at 600 volts. This can give an electric shock. (Glasgow fitted porcelain insulators to the bow ropes to prevent this.)
- Any knots or loops' other than at the end of the rope must be removed as these can lead to problems reversing the bow if caught in a tramcar body fixture or fitting.

Pantograph

- Check that the pantograph head is at right angles to the overhead wire, in the horizontal plane, and is not damaged or twisted. If the head is of the carbon strip type, check for any sign of damage to the carbon.
- Check that the pantograph ropes are secured to the pantograph and in good condition (a gentle pull on each of the ropes is advised). Care should been taken if the rope is saturated with water as the ropes are often secured to the pantograph frame which is live at 600 volts. This can give an electric shock. Any knots or loops, other than at the end of the rope, must be removed as these can prevent the pantograph being in contact with the overhead line.
- When raising the pantograph, do not allow it to hit the overhead line with force so that the carbon strip is damaged. This damage may be unseen but can later worsen with use and cause severe damage to itself and the overhead. When raising the pantograph always keep hold of the rope and let the pantograph slowly rise until the wire is reached.

6.1.3 Lifeguards

(equipment to prevent persons being run over.)

'Trigger' type, with a hinged front gate that operates a sprung-operated tray (mounted above the rails) this when released acts as a scoop. See Para 6.1.3.1 overleaf.

Inspect lifeguard installation for any damage i.e., broken or split timber work, bent or twisted metal work. Check also, clearance above ground level. It should be 4 inches = 102mm (Board of Trade ruling) particularly at the front of tray.

Before carrying out a function test of the lifeguard make sure that:

a Where folding platform steps are fitted, they are secured in the 'up' position.

b No one is on the platform above to come in contact with the resetting pedal. Carefully apply pressure to the front gate at a 'strong point' (where timber is backed with metal work i.e., at hinge straps) until the tray drops, make a mental note of the force required.

c If too much force is required, the front gate may be damaged in an impact and the tray will not drop, thus failing to provide a safeguard preventing access to the wheels.

d If a light force is required then dynamic movement of the tram and/or wind force may cause the tray to drop inadvertently. The tray should drop swiftly, usually with a loud bang, being spring fired; slow movement is a defect and must be reported to the supervisor.

e Reset the lifeguard by applying foot pressure to the reset pedal (dependent on the installation it may require some fore or aft force as well as vertical). If the lifeguard will not reset seek assistance from a supervisor.
Note: **Always check that lifeguards have been reset correctly before moving the tramcar.**
Fixed/sprung type. Fixed type can be a simple structure to act as a wheel guard by deflecting object. The sprung type can be either a sloping deflector that will move to a near vertical position when an object is contacted, or a horizontal tray that will deflect downwards when an object is contacted.

f Inspect the installation for any damage i.e., broken or split timber work, or metal work that has been damaged.

g **The 'Providence' type:** a horizontal tray extends beyond the front of the tram with a secondary tray mounted to prevent contact with the fender and dash panel, see illustration overleaf.

h Inspect installation for damage.

Preserved Lisbon tram 283 sporting a "Providence" type lifeguard in its extended position. A film exists of the American inventor demonstrating the effectiveness of his creation by standing in the way of an approaching tram! This photo was taken at Alto Sao Joa shortly after this car's superb restoration in the 1980s.

i Position tray in operating position and check ground clearance.

j Check that any stowage devices operate correctly to hold the tray upright.

6.1.3.1 Operation of 'Trigger' type lifeguard.

Fixed/sprung type

The fixed type of lifeguard can be a simple device acting as a wheel guard deflecting any object on the rails. The sprung type can be a sloping deflector held by springs and capable of moving in a more vertical position and closer to the rails when an obstruction is contacted. Alternatively, it could be formed of a horizontal metal tray held in place by springs, but capable of deflection downwards when an obstruction is encountered.

- Inspect the device for damage, e.g. broken or split timber work, bent or twisted metal components.
- Check the clearance above ground level for tray type.

"Providence" type

- This type, rarely seen today, comprises a horizontal tray made out of metal straps which extends beyond the front of the tram. A second steel mattress shaped framework is mounted vertically to prevent contact with the fender and dash panel. (See photo alongside.)

6.1.4 Boarding the Tram

Drivers should board at the platform from which they will drive. The first check is that the rails are not covered in sand – if so, the tram may be "grounded", and if you have any reason to suspect this you should jump onto the step-board, without allowing your body to form an electrical bridge to earth.

- The first priority once on board is to check that the handbrake has been fully applied, only then is it safe to walk about the tram. Don't forget to reset the lifeguard at this stage.
- If any "stop" boards or warning signs have been left on the tram, do not ignore them, enquire why?
- If you need to enter the saloon, switch on the lighting and see if the floor traps are properly in place. If the lights do not come on, or a flickering light results, assume that the tram is grounded and take appropriate action without delay (see section 5.3).

6.1.5 The Tram Interior

Before encouraging anyone else to board the tramcar the driver should first check that all floor hatches are in place, and no tools or portable equipment have been left lying in the interior. These checks should now be made:

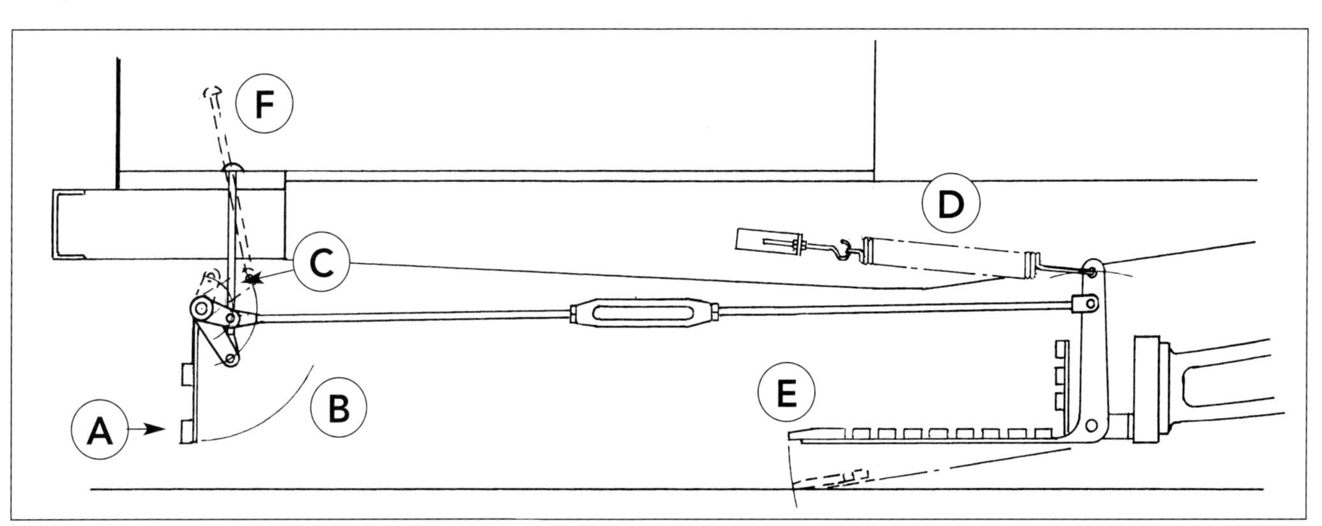

Diagram 43. Explanation of how 'trigger'-type lifeguard works. When the front gate A strikes an obstruction, it will pivot on the mounting bar through an arc B. This causes the mechanism at C to move over centre allowing spring D to pull down the tray E. At the same time the reset pedal F will come up from the floor.

- A fire extinguisher is fitted, is fully functioning, and is of the appropriate type for use with electrical equipment. (Be familiar with the various forms of extinguisher and how they are identified.)
- The tram interior is clean and presentable.
- Check underfoot for trip and slip hazards. Are all floor traps in place correctly? Ensure that there are no:
  1 Loose wear strips and step edges.
  2 Worn floor coverings.
  3 Oil or grease deposits on floor.
- Seats, clean and undamaged. Check for:
  a Sharp edges or protruding screws, which may damage clothing.
  b Chewing gum, which may soil passengers' clothes.
  c The ease of operation of reversible seats.
  d Security of fixtures and fittings (e.g. especially if sand box access covers form part of the seating.
- Covers/doors secure on electrical cupboards or boxes.
- Sand hoppers are full and dry.
- Hand-rails are securely fixed to tram body. Standee straps are not worn or damaged (if leather, check that this material has not been weakened or become brittle with age).
- Doors operate freely, and door furniture is secure.
- Opening windows are free to operate, with all fixtures and fittings secure.
- Interior generally, that there are no:
  a Loose mouldings, catches or fittings.
  b Broken or cracked windows or mirrors.
  c Dirt on window ledges that could transfer to passengers' clothing.
  d No signs of water ingress.
  e Missing or damaged light bulbs? (Do not switch on until replaced).
- Destination displays are appropriate, and the roller blind equipment functions properly. Beware of slack blinds resting on light bulbs – fire risk.
- Conductor's bell system – check position of change-over switch for bells, if fitted. Press every Bell Push as the car interior is checked out.
- Full set of portable equipment (point-iron, gong pedals, etc.) is carried.

6.1.6 Electrical and Pneumatic

Interior Lighting

Having established that there are no missing or damaged light bulbs, all the lighting circuits should be checked – including the change-over options. Drivers should remember that although traditional tram lighting uses five 110-volt bulbs, the applied voltage is 550/600. This means that if the circuit is switched on and no current flows any exposed lamp-holder will be live at 600 volts. Never attempt to change or remove a light bulb while the circuit is switched on – isolate the supply by removing the current collector. Report any defective lighting circuit to the supervisor as a car defect. Even during daytime operation lighting may be required at short notice if the weather worsens. Drivers should try out the car lighting a half-hour before dusk.

Tramcar Lights

A full service check includes:

- Head and tail-lights at both ends, operation of the change-over switches (some operators fitted as many as three – the third transfers the platform light from one end to the other!). (Historical note: Before 1930 the present rule of a white light denoting the front end, and red for the rear light did not apply. The old system was to display a red light at the front, and a green one at the rear indicating safety as the tram was travelling away from the location.).
- Side lights (sometimes referred to as marker lights), if fitted. On some designs of tram these are contained in the same lamp box as the rear lights. Red bulbs or bulbs behind a red filter shining through the clear glass of the white side lights.
- Trafficators (direction indicators) at both ends, if fitted.
- Brake lights (both ends), if fitted, and then only following activation of the compressed-air braking system.

The Circuit Breaker

Before checking the operation of the circuit breaker, first check that the controller key is not in either controller, and that all covers are secure protecting the controllers and/or all electrical switches and cupboards.

Operate the circuit breaker with care. Should there be a fault within the traction system it could open under overload conditions while the driver's hand is on the handle!

It is recommended that the circuit breaker is closed and then opened by operating the handle gently. On opening (or tripping) the breaker a clunking sound will indicate a rapid opening of the contacts. Failure to make this sound may indicate a problem with the tripping mechanism – a potentially serious failure that is to be reported as a defect.

The Canopy Switch

This may look like a circuit breaker, but is a simple switch lacking the overload protection mechanism. Fitted to some trams (at one end only, and usually before World War I), it was used in conjunction with a traction fuse. Located at the same position as a circuit breaker, it provides the same facility for the driver to isolate the traction power if the controller jams on a power notch. Drivers should advise the conductor if such a unit is fitted to a tram, and explain the difference in its function.

The Controllers

Function checks of the circuit breaker should take place before the operating checks of the controller – always switch off the adjacent circuit breaker before moving the main handle of the controller. This is an important safeguard when testing the "rear" platform controller – this should only be done after the circuit breaker on the rear platform has been switched off.

Before testing the controller check that:

- The controller is securely mounted and fastened to the tram structure.
- Its front cover or lid is correctly fitted and locked in place.
- The top plate (casting), power handle, the caps to reverser barrel and motor cut out switch are all secure.
- The motor cut out switch has not been operated, and all motors are switched in.

To test the controller (after ensuring that the adjacent circuit breaker/canopy switch is in the "Off" position, and the parking brake applied) drivers should:

- Insert the controller key in the reverser barrel cap, and turn to the direction of travel. N.B. If parked close to another tram select the direction away from the adjacent tram! Much less embarrassment or damage will result from any unwanted movement.

- Move the controller handle through all the power notches until the mechanical stop is reached. Then return it to the "Off" position.
- Move the handle through all the brake notches until the stop is reached, and then return to the "Off" position.
- Move the controller key to the opposite direction of travel, and repeat the above two stages of checking the power and brake notches.
- Remove the controller key.

Note: If the controller handle is difficult to operate, especially if notches appear mechanically blocked, this is an indication that the controller is defective and should be reported as such. If the handle cannot be moved beyond the Series notches, check that the motor cut-out switch is properly positioned at the 'All in' location. Remember too, that with some controllers if motors are isolated in this way, the rheostatic braking can be non-effective.

Trams with Air Systems and Air-Brakes

On trams with air-brakes, drivers must when switching on the compressor listen to the equipment carefully. If the motor runs but no increase in pressure is forthcoming, the equipment should be switched off and the defect reported. When the pressure builds up, the driver must remain vigilant that the cut-out switch operates at the maximum working pressure (80PSI to 90PSI or between 5 and 6 BAR). In the case of trams fitted with electro-pneumatic switchgear, testing of the control equipment should be done after the air system is fully charged. The checks listed above in the paragraphs headed "Controllers" being carried out as applicable.

6.1.7 Miscellaneous Equipment

Dropping sand in the depot building should be avoided – this could cause "grounding". Do test the sanding equipment outdoors. Only trams carrying a trolley cane (i.e. those not fitted with trolley ropes) should be allowed to use a trolley reverser feature in the overhead wiring. When checking a trolley cane (commonly known as a bamboo pole!) beware of splinters that can be razor sharp. Check also for cracks in the bamboo, cleanliness, and loose fittings. Never leave the depot without a trolley cane, and never move the tram with the cane attached to the trolley pole.

For safety reasons it is common practice to leave individual depot tracks' overhead wires normally switched off, until power is needed, lockable switches being provided for this purpose. When power is required the person operating the switches should first check that no isolation board or personal pad-lock has been attached to the switch, he/she must then shout a warning alerting anyone nearby: e.g. "Power on track 4!" And then listen for any reply before closing the switch. Anyone switching on power to move a tram must remember to switch off power and to lock the switch cupboard before leaving the location. It is especially important to follow this procedure whenever open-topped trams are parked in a particular depot siding. Inside a depot building the overhead wiring is usually lower than normal. Never leave the current switched on when the track is unattended by staff, and staff should not access any tramcar's open top deck in the depot when the power is switched on. Carry out checks on the open top deck and retrieve the stored trolley rope from up there, before switching on the power.

6.2 Tramcar Movements

On any tramway system the majority of all accidents will occur in the depot facilities. Movements in sidings and shunting operations are deemed so potentially dangerous that many operators insist that staff wear "high visibility" warning jackets when walking in sidings – even during the brief walk to board their tram! Heritage tramways are often reluctant to adopt modern safety practices, thinking that orange or yellow jackets do not fit the nostalgic image. However, it should be remembered that whilst most tramway operators go to great lengths to keep the public out of depots and sidings, heritage tramways often encourage the public to enter depot buildings in order to view tramcars not being used in service. An invitation to walk into depot areas must most surely include a duty of care to the unwary. The public must be assumed to have no experience of how quickly trams can change from being a dormant giant to a moving monster! There is no revving of engines to warn bystanders, the movement of a controller from off to notch one is all that is needed. Crews therefore must give adequate warning e.g. "Please stand clear, this tram is about to move!" and make a liberal use of the gong or whistles.

The conductor (or other member of staff) should be deployed to watch blind spots, or other areas out of the driver's field of vision. Adequate supervision is the best prevention of accidents. Once the tram has moved and there is ample track space (do not stop on any dead section of overhead wiring!) the hand brake (and air brake, if fitted) should be used in order to test their effectiveness. On trams equipped with air brakes the hand-brake should not be used as a service brake (except when parking the tram) unless it is used to hold back the tram while inching forward in confined spaces. The same rule applies to trams fitted with equipment deemed suitable for the electric brake to be used as the service brake.

Some depots were constructed with traversers (and turntables) to save the expense of complicated pointwork. Americans refer to the former as a transfer table, and many London County Council Tramway depots were built with this feature. A typical traverser was built with a pit containing rails (on which the traverser runs), laid at right angles to the tram storage tracks. This feature can be a danger to the unwary visitor, and provides a hazard for tramcars unable to stop short of the pit! Best practice is to first position the traverser, then move the tram – the driver having checked that all rails ends are in close alignment. The tram's driver should position his car centrally on the traverser carriage, apply the hand-brake, and check that sufficient clearance exists between the tram and any obstructions. Before moving the traverser the tram's current collector must be lowered and secured. Operation of the traverser itself may be restricted to specially trained personnel. These recommendations should apply also to moving trams on turntables.

If any of the start of day checks listed above show that equipment is defective, missing, or damaged, then the tram is deemed to be UNSERVICEABLE. Any malfunctioning component that affects the safety of the vehicle is to be reported by filling in a defect report-sheet, and the tram **must not be taken into service**.

The traverser at the National Tramway Museum's Depot at Crich.

Permission to leave the depot with your tram must be gained from the Officer-in-Charge. This may be implicit when on a scheduled duty, and the crew has been issued with a running board (timetable). A telephone or short-wave radio may be used to contact the person in authority. It is good practice to repeat verbal instructions back to the person giving them. This safeguards the accuracy of the message. Good radio discipline will be detailed in local instructions. Always remember that radio communication is not secure, and if confidentiality is an issue, use the telephone.

Even at this stage the tram is not completely checked out – the sanders need to be checked at a location where the accumulation of sand will not cause a problem. Finally, the electric brake must be tested at a reasonable speed from both controllers; only then can the driver be satisfied that the tram is fully in order.

Drivers should never use any parallel notches until the tests are completed satisfactorily. The author, when still a novice driver, once forgot this rule while road-testing a multiple unit tram whose driver had reported that the unit would not accelerate properly. It did, right up to 50km/h, then the reported (but intermittent) fault manifested itself in the braking notches, resulting in total failure of the electric brake. Application of the handbrake and track-brakes seemed at the time little more than a gesture. Fortunately the traffic lights ahead changed to green and the big tanker on the crossing moved off before the tram and I ground to a halt in the middle of the road!

When crew are relieved at meal breaks etc., the driver handing over the car must inform his colleague(s) of any aspect or detail which he/she is not totally happy with. This should apply especially to items that are not serious enough to condemn the tram, but may well be in a worsening process and soon become a matter for concern, (e.g. brakes stiff, controller handle not moving freely, etc.).

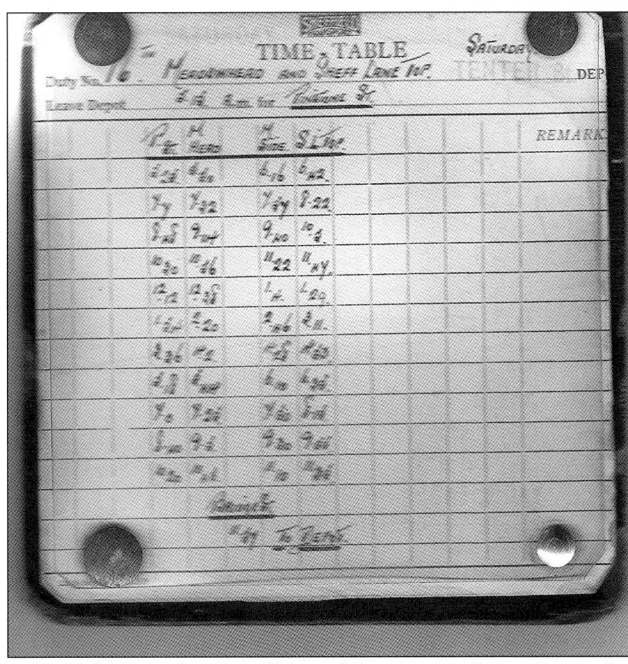

A Sheffield "Running Board" issued from Tenter Street Depot for the Meadowhead and Sheffield Lane Top Service. The board was carried in a special holder fitted inside the windscreen, and the reverse of the board was given a number and a distinctive colour indicating the duty. This would be used by inspectors wishing to identify the tram's duty and service without the need to board the car.

CHAPTER 7

Everyday Driving

7.1 Normal Service

Most tramcars in normal service operate to a scheduled timetable; other trams on special duties (workshop test runs, transfer trips between depots, private hire, etc.) must leave their depot only after permission to do so has been granted by the officer in charge of the control room, or dispatcher. This rule enables supervisory staff to know the number and type of extra cars at large on the system – an important piece of information in the event of a traffic crisis.

It could be said that tram drivers operate within a set of closed parameters: they are governed by a timetable, must obey operating regulations and conform to speed limits. Modern tramcars are equipped with "black box" data recorders which, when downloaded, can reveal not only speeds, but also the operation of most driving controls from track-brakes to sanders. Drivers of heritage trams might not have the same degree of electronic monitoring, but accurate measurement of speed (and therefore proof that speed restrictions are being respected) can be provided by the use of radar speed guns. Although heritage trams may lack speedometers, experienced drivers can judge speeds with a fair degree of accuracy.

Drivers need to concentrate fully on the driving activity. On trams without a separate driving position, they should not allow themselves to be distracted by passengers wishing to indulge in conversation. A polite: "I'll answer your question when we next stop" is the reply. To prevent accidents to children, front end bulkhead doors should always be kept shut (unless summer gates or barriers are in place). On trams equipped for one person operation ticket issuing and checking must only be done when the tram is stationary.

The tram driver is expected to drive economically, not wasting energy by unnecessary fast running or excessive acceleration. A good driver will only use power on level track for just one third of the journey between stops: acceleration up to line speed, one third; coasting, one third; and braking, one third. The use of power on a falling gradient should be restricted to a brief period when leaving a stop; any other application of power is wasteful and unnecessary.

There is a correct way and wrong way of taking corners when driving a tram.

This is particularly noticeable when driving a four-wheeled tram! With this kind of vehicle, simply coasting into a bend will lead to the tram lurching around the curve, making it very uncomfortable for passengers. The correct way is to brake before the curve, then apply moderate power to draw the tram around the curve. This method will keep the tram's suspension (i.e. springing) taut and lessen its capability to bounce and lurch.

On tramways where trailer haulage is commonplace (e.g. The Isle of Man's Manx Electric Railway), a more comfortable ride will be produced if the couplings can be kept taut. This is why the M.E.R. drivers do not switch off power when approaching climbing curves. Their drivers are allowed to move the controller handle smartly back from full Parallel to the full Series position. I have only ever seen this done elsewhere once and that was fifty years ago on the Belgian Vicinal coastal tramway – again a line with (in those days) trailer haulage. This practice of not switching the controller handle back to the 'Off' position is definitely not recommended for universal application.

Coupling and uncoupling trailers should be done in a safe manner. See Section 9.5 of this book. Widely regarded as the safest form of mechanical coupling is the coupling system described below. It was invented nearly a hundred years ago by the Manager of Krefeld tramways in the Rhineland, and is called the Albert Coupling. One of its strengths is that it does not require the 'shunter' to be involved with moving the vehicles being coupled up.

Widely used for both vehicle and emergency couplings on current generation tramcars, it is deployed as follows:

The vehicles are parked at a distance suitable for making the coupling, i.e. distance 'X' on diagram 44a, with the couplings set to one side as shown.

Second operation, with the vehicles still distance 'X' apart, is to remove pin P1. It should be noted that the pins have a hinged C shaped device that prevents the pin from being removed/coming out when the coupling is made, and are usually connected to the coupling head by a retaining chain.

Move the couplers through their arc of movement until pin P1 can be located in hole 'b' and hole 'c' on the other, see diagram 44b. N.B. Pin P2 must not be placed in holes 'a' or 'b'

The final stage in the coupling operation is to move the vehicles apart until the couplings are in line and pin P2 can be placed in hole marked 'd' and 'a' (see diagram 44c).

Many tramway operators went to the expense of fitting car-meters. These were similar to domestic electricity meters but engineered for use on direct current. By regularly recording the meter readings wasteful drivers could easily be identified, and those who drove economically could be rewarded with a bonus. The meter was a useful source of information for technical personnel who could identify a rogue traction motor by its voracious appetite for current.

Brake lights are another feature rarely fitted to these veterans. In the past drivers kept a healthy distance when following another tramcar, in case the one in front made an emergency stop. Failure to keep a safe separation was known in tramway-man's language as "close-poling". The prescribed safe distance is the length of track between three overhead masts (i.e. poles) at normal spacing on plain track. The only exception to this rule was while at low speed approaching tram stops, or traffic signals.

When a tram has to stop at an unexpected location, hazard warning or rear lights must be used to provide warning to any following tramcar. After dusk in the event of a power failure the conductor should be stationed at the rear with a battery torch to protect the car from any approaching vehicle.

Restricted clearances and blind corners demand a reduction in speed and an increase in the driver's vigilance. The gong should be sounded when passing parked vehicles if they are close to the tram track, and also when passing

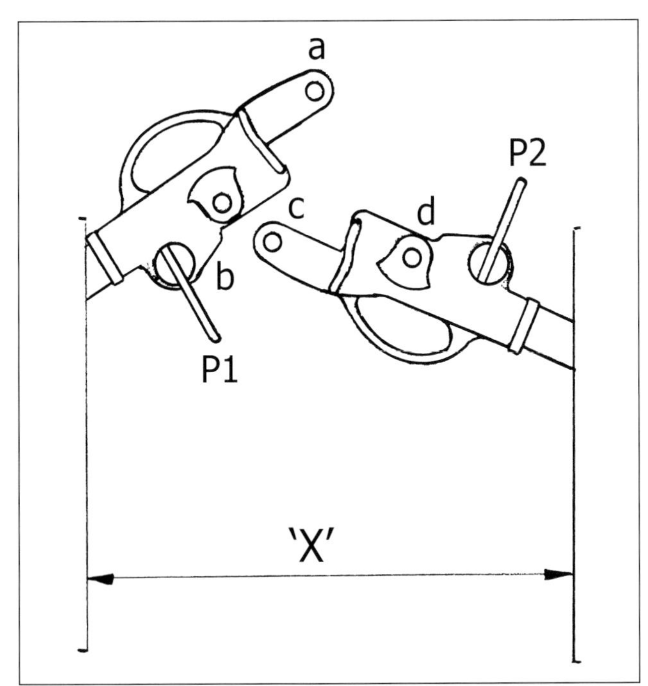

Diagram 44a: Initial location of vehicles to be coupled.

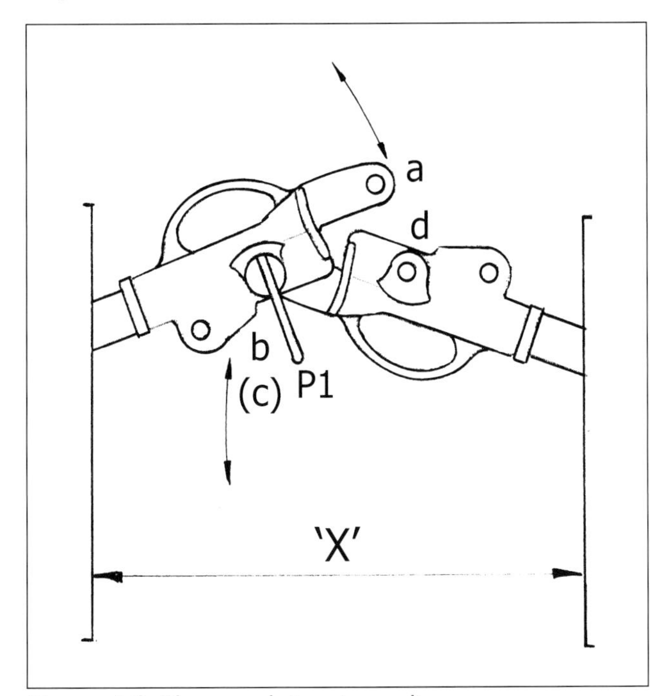

Diagram 44b: The second stage in coupling up.

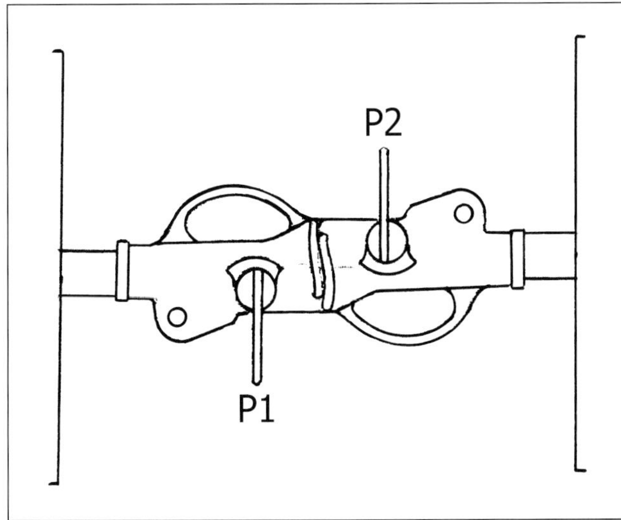

Diagram 44c: Fully made Albert coupling

other trams at speed on a street tramway. (Trams pass one another much closer than other road vehicles.) A pedestrian may wait for one tram to pass and dash out in front of the one coming in the opposite direction. Drivers should never assume that sounding the gong is sufficient – the pedestrian may have hearing difficulties, and the construction worker near the track may not hear because of noisy machinery nearby.

Drivers should never take risks with brakes: braking performance may vary from one trip to the next, and rail conditions may change rapidly. Never attempt to stop close to another vehicle from speed with just one brake application. Better to stop short and inch forward, perhaps using the hand brake to hold back movement of the car.

Tram drivers should beware of all point-work, and never reverse over unseen point blades. Drivers should always stop and set the point blades with a point iron. Staff should never assume that the tram's wheels have pushed the point blades over, they seldom if ever do!

7.2 Permanent Way Work

When work is being carried out on the tramway or associated equipment, and the ordinary service continues, drivers should approach the location of any such work with extreme caution. Operators working at the site may be so engrossed in the job that they remain unaware of approaching vehicles. Drivers should always sound the gong or horn, and then if no acknowledgement is received the tram must stop and await a sign that it is safe to proceed. If a stop sign is displayed the driver must not proceed until the stop sign is removed and a clear signal is given that it is safe to proceed.

Drivers should beware of tools and other objects left close to the track. There is only limited room under any tramcar, and anything left between the rails may damage under-floor equipment. An engineering bolt left in the rail-groove may cause a serious derailment.

Great care must be exercised when driving trams over open track-work (i.e. after the road surface has been removed). Drivers should remember that if the lifeguard mechanism has a spring-operated tray, once triggered it will come down to the rail-head and will act as a blade rather than a scoop. An accident of this kind happened in Edinburgh over fifty years ago, with fatal consequences.

In certain cases when overhead line work is being carried out, it may be necessary for the tram to coast under a section of overhead while the current collector is pulled clear of the wire.

Temporary speed restrictions will be marked by signs showing the maximum speed in mph (or kph, in the case of new tramways – the letters TSR marking out temporary speed restrictions, as distinct from more permanent ones). Good practice demands that termination boards be also installed to mark the end of such restrictions, these usually display the letters TSR crossed out with a diagonal line.

7.3 At the Terminus

At termini when trailing through points with blades held by springs in the opposite direction than that of the arriving tram, it is the driver's elementary precaution to ensure that the tram is brought to a stop with all its wheels well clear of the point blades. Secondly, as debris can prevent point blades returning to their proper position, even under spring pressure, a visual inspection of the point blades is an important precaution for every driver.

Drivers should ensure that the tram is properly braked before starting the change ends routine – is the airbrake pressure high enough, and not leaking off? Any rear-view mirror should be retracted, hand-brake secure and in its restraint if fitted; pedals removed or disengaged, the folding step lowered. The barrier chain can be left in place until removed by the conductor when he/she wishes passengers to board.

The driver should disregard all diversions and proceed immediately to the "new" platform. First the brake must be checked, if the tram is air-braked it is better to transfer the brake to the hand-brake unless departure is immediate. On hand-brake fitted trams the conductor will release the brake from the rear platform when the tram departs. Pedals inserted ready for action, and step raised, barrier chain put in place, and the rear view mirror adjusted; these are all important preparations before moving.

Furthermore, the driver should check that the current collector is in the correct position to start off (dependent on type of collector and the overhead equipment installed). The driver should also consider which action now follows:

Bow reversal, or use of a trolley reverser. Is it single or double trolley wire? Do special procedures for turning the trolley on open toppers apply?

Much thought and debate took place at Crich twenty years ago concerning the safest practice to adopt in the change-ends procedure to be applied when reversing hand-brake trams. (Using modern parlance, we carried out a risk assessment!) It was agreed that the hand-brake application used to stop the moving tram on entering the terminus, was more reliable, i.e. it had stopped the tram, and it was applied by the driver. The alternative of swapping the brake while the tram was stationary, and allowing the conductor to apply the brake at the old rear platform was deemed less safe. It is not widely known that under certain conditions as passengers are allowed to board, and the tramcar's springs move or sink under the extra weight, the geometry of the hand-brake rigging can be so changed that the brake is loosened.

The departure routine adopted is that the driver, having seen that the conductor is on the rear platform and the boarding of passengers finished, moves the controller key to "forward", and rings the gong. The conductor checks that all is clear for departure then rings the bell twice, and the driver makes the final checks:

- Look in the rear-view mirror that no one is attempting to board.
- No one is standing too close, or could be intending to run alongside the tram.
- No person is sitting on the front fender (a favourite spot for little Johnny to have his photo taken).
- The road ahead is clear.

If all these are clear, then the driver puts on the first notch of power. The conductor now releases the hand-brake fully and places the handle in the restraint. If at any time from this instant a stop is required, the driver will apply the handbrake at his/her end. The driver at the completion of the procedure is well advised to "gather in" the handbrake at the new platform, and lock in the pawl at the position where the brake begins to have effect.

Drivers should never move a tramcar on any paved area (street or depot yard) without the "safe to start" two bell signal from the conductor. At termini or in the depot yard no passengers may be allowed to remain unsupervised on a tramcar. In the event of a physical needs break one member of staff must inform the other of the need to leave the tram. Both members of staff may only leave their loaded tram if another staff member (e.g. Duty Inspector) is able to supervise it.

Care should be taken when a tram is fitted with a buzzer in place of a bell. It can be confusing if insufficient time is given between pulses and the signal becomes ambiguous. Any unclear signal should not be acted upon. If in doubt, stop the tram.

The Bell Code

One Bell:	Stop at next stop **or** Cancel "Safe to Start" signal.
Two Bells:	"Safe to Start"
Three Bells:	Car full, do not stop at any request stop until a one-bell signal is given.

Multiple ringing of bell: emergency stop required.

Stamping on the roof above the driver's head by the conductor is not considered good or safe practice. A whistle or verbal instruction should be employed if the normal bell is not available for use.

A final word about tram stops. When a driver approaches a stop already occupied by a preceding tram, and the second tram has insufficient space, it is far safer to hold back well clear of the stop. It should deter even the most determined member of the public from attempting to alight if the tram is not at the stopping place.

7.4 Poor Weather Conditions

In exceptional weather conditions special considerations apply. Where a tramway has been constructed on high ground with an exposed profile, it would be safer not to operate double-deck cars in high winds.

When electrical storms threaten it would be prudent to advise passengers not to travel on open top decks or balconies. The supervising officer should be kept advised of any worsening weather conditions, so that an informed decision can be made regarding whether or not to withdraw certain trams from service.

When heavy rains cause water ingress in close proximity to electrical equipment, or cabinets where such items are fitted, the potential danger must be recognised and appropriate measures taken. E.g. evacuate passengers, park the tram in a convenient place and lower the current collector. Trams should never be driven through flood water, and in the case of a parked tram being affected by standing water, the current collector must be lowered immediately.

When electrical storms occur drivers should use series notches only and switch on all car lighting. Should the tram be struck by lightning, this is to be regarded as an electrical fire. The current collector should be tied down, any signs of combustion looked for, and where necessary a fire extinguisher used to prevent further conflagration. The safety of passengers must remain paramount, and a risk assessment made concerning the wisdom of evacuating the tram. During an electrical storm it may be more dangerous to remove the passengers from the tram and leave them standing on open ground. As with any suspected fire do not put the current collector back on the wire until technical staff have inspected and cleared the tram for further service.

In times of fog or poor visibility caused by falling snow, car lights and lighting should be switched on, and drivers must reduce speed. On double track this means that the speed must be no higher than that at which the tram can be stopped within one half of the limit of visibility. On single

Woltersdorf, near Berlin, in winter 1984. The tram, later museum car 7, is a prototype of the K.S.W. design for a wartime standard tramcar. Twenty years ago it was still in active service, even if only used as a spare car. It is now preserved along with a matching trailer. Photo: G. Krueger

line sections (or sections of interlaced track) the speed must be no more than that from which a stop in one-third of the distance of visibility can be made.

Driving through snow can cause a build up of snow on the lifeguard gate, causing the tray to trip. Driving with one foot against the lifeguard resetting pedal may remedy this. The same technique may also be used during high winds. Do not let too much snow build up on the lifeguard equipment – the weight of it may break the wooden slats. Use a brush periodically to remove the snow. Some first generation tramways fitted snow chains to hold up the lifeguard tray, and effectively disabled the equipment when snow was present. It is doubtful if railway safety authorities would permit this in the 21st century!

Driving along snow-covered track calls for special driving skills – skills that have to be learnt on the job. No driving school course known to the author includes this! On older trams the secret is to lightly apply the hand-brake, and so inhibit the wheels from spinning. The lightly applied brake shoes will also warm the wheel's tyres. Modern trams only have stored spring brakes which rules out this strategy. In my experience the worst offenders (for wheel spin on snow) among trams are those fitted with tandem drive. This uses just one traction motor per bogie. These are placed longitudinally, and have two gear-boxes (i.e. a drive to each axle). This was a standard feature among Düwag-built trams in the 1960s – except in Dortmund where winters are cold. When purchasing new articulated trams in 1959-64 their Tramway Department wisely specified the fitting of conventional traction motors driving one axle each.

Drivers should beware of points buried under snow. Never assume that all will be well under the blanket of snow. Use the snow-broom provided to clear the points, and see for yourself that the blades are correctly positioned.

Finally, when snow melts an abundance of water remains. Think of the damage that may be caused to traction motors if too much snow penetrates the air inlets and collects inside the motors.

7.5 Single Line Working

Whilst the latest German Tramways Construction and Use Regulations (BO Strab) prescribe that all new tramways should be built as double track lines, exceptions can be granted. The latest tramways built in Britain include sections of single-line tramway; these are protected not only by automatic signals, but feature "SPAD" (i.e. Signal Passed At Danger) alarms. This, in the event of a tramcar entering a single line section against a "stop" signal, will set off flashing blue alarm signals along the single track. Once this happens all trams in section must stop.

On tramways built around the year 1900 it was often permitted to operate a section of single-track between passing places by using an on-sight system, inbound trams having priority before midday and outbound trams afterwards. If longer sections of single-track were built, or it was not possible to see from one loop to the next, some form of regulation was required. The simplest of these is by use of a distinctive staff or token. (See section 2.6.4, page 25 for more details.) Complications arise when more than one tram may wish to enter the section before a tram in the opposite direction arrives, and/or if more trams travel in one direction than the other, and a balanced frequency does not apply.

To cope with drawbacks like those described above, electric signalling came into being. Usually employing contact skates on the overhead wire, the first skate would put in a demand – if the single line was unoccupied a "proceed" signal would light up. A second skate located beyond the signal and just before the end of the double

EXPRESS Freitag, 27. September 19

er Stunden brauchten Feuerwehrmänner, bis der tote Straßenbahnfahrer Karl Schallenberg aus dem Chaos befreit war. Bilder: Großpitz

Tote auf Linie 7!

Schwerstes Unglück der KVB seit Kriegsende - 14 Opfer

exp Köln — Punkt 16.43 rasten zwischen orz und Zündorf zwei Züge der KVB ineinnder! Die Bilanz: Fahrer Karl Schallenberg 1) aus Porz und Signalmann Adolf Franz (29)

Dies ist das schwerste Unglück der Kölner Verkehrsbetriebe seit Kriegsende.

Um 13.03 Uhr fällt die automatische Ampelanlage

16.43 Uhr: In Höhe der Float-Glaswerke an der Poststraße prallen die beiden Züge, einer aus Zündorf, einer aus Porz kommend, mit hoher Geschwindigkeit auf-

Todesangst stemmte ich mic mit beiden Händen auf de Vordersitz. Ein Vater, de vor mir saß, drückte sei Kind ganz fest an sich, u es zu schützen. Ich merkt

This press cutting describes a double fatal accident in Cologne when operating procedures were ignored and two Düwag cars hit head on at speed on a single line section.

The inbound tramcar was empty apart from the driver and a signalling technician – they were both killed in the accident. What happened was that the automatic signalling system failed earlier. The signalling technician was called for and the back up procedure called into play. This meant drivers, on arrival at the single line section (or waiting departure from the terminal loop) had to use the dedicated signal phone to request a path authorised by the dispatcher. He regulated the traffic on the single line by writing departure and arrival details in a register. After the signal system had been sorted (the relay box at the outer terminus was to blame), the technician said something like "that's fixed it then" on boarding the waiting car at the terminal loop. Having seen the green aspect now showing, the driver set off unaware that an outbound car had been given permission to enter the 2km single line section, which had a high-speed curve halfway with limited vision.

The technician should, of course, have informed the dispatcher first that the signals were once again functioning, and the driver failed to wait for his permission to revert to normal procedures. To crown it all, after the carnage, the use of gas-cutting torches caused one of the then new trams to burn completely out. This was one of a number of single-line incidents during the 'sixties. The KVB doubled the section of track concerned only 18 months later.

track would register that the line was now occupied. Just beyond the points at the far end of the single line a third skate would detect the tram leaving the section, and return the system to "unoccupied" status.

Any system using relays and contacts etc. not only needs a safe fall-back procedure to be ready for instant use, but also has another disadvantage. Drivers soon discover how an illicit second car can follow on without waiting for the first to clear the section. Cologne's drivers on the now disappeared single line sections were well skilled at pulling down their tram's pantograph and coasting under skates! Dedicated signal telephones directly linking hand-sets in boxes on signal masts with control rooms are essential means of communication. During any signal failures verbal instructions to drivers are given by the control room dispatchers. All conversations are electronically recorded and the dispatchers must maintain a written register of tram movements.

Remember that all verbal communications by radio or telephone are considered to be safety critical in the event of an accident or incident. Drivers and other members of staff must use the protocol they have been taught.

Finally, a reminder that the margin of safety for driving on single track sections is a speed from which the tram can be stopped within one-third of the limit of visibility. See Section 7.4. Driving in adverse weather, para.5.

On 19 October 2006 I drove an ex-Köln Düwag in Konya, Turkey. It was the first time that I had driven one of these cars since 1970 and was so pleased when I got it right first time. Amongst the group of enthusiasts on the special car were two present-day qualified Cologne drivers who gave me a round of applause at the end of my stint!

CHAPTER 8

Bringing the Tram back to Depot

All tram depots have a different track layout. A common way of sorting trams as they return to base is first to sort out those that are due for maintenance on the following day, and park them in the workshop area or on a designated track. Second, trams should be stabled according to their route allocation, using two or three sidings for each route served. The person allocating cars to each new duty roster can therefore pick the cars at the front for the first duties due to commence on the next day, and follow the sequence according to position of parking.

In a museum setting the choice of depot road may be determined by the type of current collector fitted to the tram, and /or the radius of the access curves to particular tracks. There may also be issues around limited clearances. (Bogie-cars may derail or be totally unsuitable when subjected to sharp curves.) In some instances the need to display a particular tram for public viewing may be a factor.

A bogie car entering Arco de Cego Depot, Lisbon in 1983.

The speed of the run to the depot must not exceed the permitted line speed.

It is good practice to display 'Depot' on the destination blinds, or turn them to a blank indication if no suitable display exists.

It may be necessary to coast into the depot yard if a bow collector is fitted – these cannot be turned in the depot yard because often the overhead wiring is lower than normal. In such cases the driver must ensure that the bow is turned and tied down before coasting in.

On air-braked cars it is essential that the reserves of air are fully charged before removing the current collector from the wire.

Drivers should not rely on the effectiveness of hand-brakes fitted to trams with air-brakes; often these are connected to one truck only and are designed solely for use as a parking brake.

During the journey through the depot yard the driver must visually check that each set of points are correctly set for the stabling road, ensuring too, that no other tram has been parked too close to point-work and stands foul of the swept path of your tram. Drivers must remain alert too for other depot movements, which may conflict.

With trolley equipped cars the conductor should be deployed to monitor the progress of the trolley through the various frogs, with whistle ready to give a stop signal. He/she should not hold the trolley rope, nor should they walk behind the tram watching the pole (and fall over items on the ground!). Never ever wrap the trolley rope around the arm or hand – it can inflict injuries.

Once the succession of points has been passed and the tram is on plain track once more, the tram should be stopped and the bow collector raised. The bow will now be in the "wrong" direction and being pushed. It is important that the tram is driven slowly to the place where the tram is to be cleaned and later to its parking location.

Cleaning the tram is an all-important fire-precaution and should be done meticulously before the tram is parked up. A discarded cigarette end can smoulder under other rubbish if left undiscovered, and burst into flames hours later when everyone has gone home.

All trams must stop before entering any building (depot or workshop). This is to ensure the safety of those working inside who probably cannot hear an approaching tram. It also proves that the brakes are effective before entering a confined space. The driver must check that any doors are fully opened and well clear of the tram's swept path. If door locking mechanisms are provided, these should be locked to prevent any gusts of wind moving doors unexpectedly.

The overhead line can now be switched on (see section 4.1) and the conductor or other staff member deployed to provide supervision of any blind spots. Audible warnings e.g. "Tramcar entering track 4" and liberal use of the audible warning device (e.g. gong), should be followed by a pause to listen for any warning response. If no response is heard, only then should the tram be driven slowly into the shed.

When parking or moving the tram at close quarters,

always stop short and then inch forward using a lightly applied hand-brake to hold back the car's movement.

In any area frequented by the public trams should not be parked leaving gaps between tramcars wide enough for someone to squeeze through. They might be doing this when a tram further along the track causes a shunt, which progresses down the line of parked tramcars like an old loose-fitted goods train, and causes severe injury to the unfortunate visitor.

With the aid of the conductor, bring the tram to within two or three inches of its neighbour – after checking that the fenders are the only things protruding. Beware of hinged windscreens left open, or overhanging trolley poles!

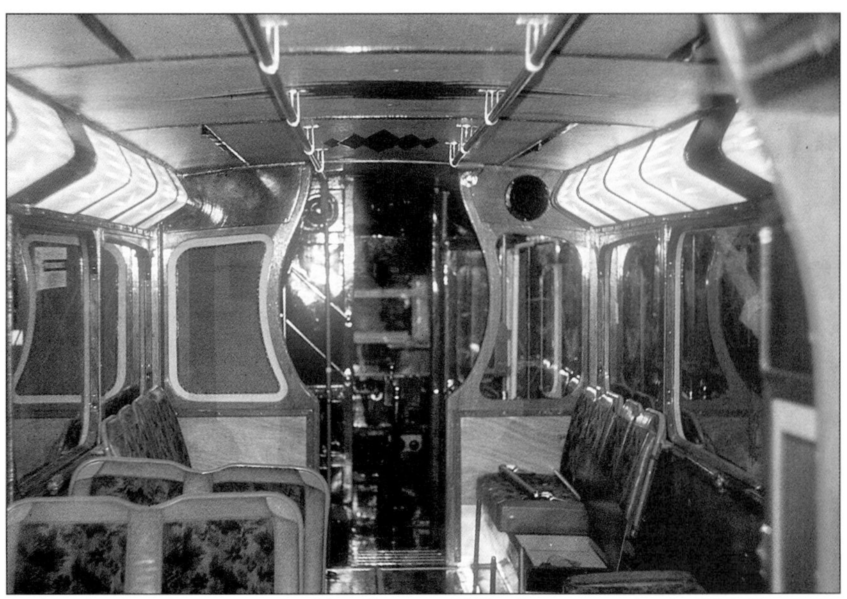

A gleaming interior is presented by Glasgow 1282 after restoration in 1978/9.

When trams are to be parked, many operators prefer that the controls are shut down in a way that will facilitate a speedy evacuation of trams in the event of a fire. The circuit breaker at the platform furthest away from the depot doorway should be left switched on, while at the platform nearest the depot doorway, the circuit breaker is switched "Off" and the hand-brake applied there (after releasing the air-brake where fitted).

Drivers should remember to switch off all lights and lighting, compressor and heating (where fitted). Remove all portable equipment including the point iron, gong and sand pedals, and the controller key and brake valve handle. These must be placed in a safe place, away from thieves.

The trolley rope, if fitted, should be placed out of harm's way – but crews should only access the open top deck of a tram after the power has been switched off on the track concerned.

Some tramway operators insisted that drivers drained the air system on their tram when stabling. Doing this daily clears the system of the water that tends to gather in the main reservoir, and keeps the drain cock well exercised. However, modern safety standards may not take kindly to blasting down the depot floor under each tram in the confined space. The operation creates a high noise level and may cause debris to fly around. It is strongly recommended that a full risk assessment is made and the procedure agreed be followed most carefully.

In some depots jumper cables are used if, for example, a tram becomes isolated from power after stopping with its current collector on a "dead section". This apparatus may consist of two bamboo trolley canes connected by a length of heavy-duty cable. After lowering the current collector and securely tying it clear of the overhead (or anything else), one of the canes is hooked to a conducting part of the current collector, and made secure. Then and only then may the other bamboo cane be hooked onto the live overhead wire. It is imperative that an experienced member of staff must supervise both bamboo poles, and be in position to remove the (live) pole from the overhead wire as swiftly as possible.

Staff must remain alert that the cable carrying 600 volts is not damaged by being run over. This entire procedure is fraught with danger, should only be attempted by experienced staff, and away from any public presence. Although it has been included here as an option for moving stranded trams, it does not come with any recommendation from the author of this book. A much safer alternative is to push the tram back on to a live section, either with another tram, or by human muscle-power! The use of jumper cables must be the subject of a risk assessment that will highlight the need for written procedures, and staff training in the use thereof. Keeping the equipment under lock and key will restrict access.

Finally, close all tramcar doors, place rope barriers across entrances (if used), shut windows with the exception of two small windows to allow ventilation and the early release of smoke in the event of fire. This will give an early detection of fire by the building's smoke detectors.

Drivers and conductors who are volunteers involved with museum operations are probably required to complete and sign a form that their tram has been cleaned and any defects have been noted. If this form is not completed and handed in, the particular tram may have to be withdrawn from serviceable status. Defects will be assumed, in the absence of evidence stating otherwise. After returning any items borrowed at the start of the shift back to the operations office, the crew may now sign off.

8.1 Other Duties

There can be few greater privileges than being involved in the training of new drivers. This may be as simply a supervising driver, enabling a trainee to get sufficient practice during the advanced part of the training programme, or as a qualified instructor. However, driving instructors are the butt of many "in-house" jokes, an example I heard in Berlin being: "How do you know when an instructor has finished his shift?" Answer: "When he takes his hands out of his pockets for the first time that day!"

It is more stressful than is realised. Not only does the instructor have to concentrate mentally as though he is driving the tram, but also has to monitor and compare the performance of the trainee with what is good driving practice. During the training sessions for the 1988 Glasgow Garden Festival an emergency stop signal was given to test the trainee's skill in stopping. I braced myself for a sharp deceleration, but was thrown almost literally off balance when the person on the controls swung the controller handle around not into the braking notches, but to the full parallel power position!

As I observed during the three-month driver training course in Cologne, the instructor needs a good sense of humour and endless reserves of patience. My instructor in

1968 had been a training officer in the Wehrmacht during WWII, and had lost none of his parade ground talents in the mean-time. Making one mistake was pardonable, but committing the same error twice was greeted by a 90 decibel rebuke. But at least, he had a sense of humour; on one occasion a lorry driver had stopped to let me cross the main carriageway with the school car. On passing his cab I raised my right arm to acknowledge his kindness. Whereupon the instructor asked me if I had been a member of the Partei!

Finally, here is an aspect of instructors' duties that is not widely known about. When a new design of tram is delivered to the operator, or, in the case of museum tramways, a newly restored tramcar is ready for use, driving instructors are routinely involved behind the scenes.

Having reached a consensus concerning whether the tramcar conforms with its specification, the next stage concerning museum trams is to investigate what modifications became necessary during its operating career. (Any return to the "as new" condition may reverse modifications deemed necessary as experience with the car was gathered during its first introduction into service.) The first priority is to make a safety audit and risk assessment. This may dismay the purists when, for example, extra railings are deemed necessary to enhance the safety of passengers. Other matters such as evacuation procedures need careful scrutiny. Can all exit doors be opened without delay?

Once the tram has passed its static testing, engineers will carry out test runs on the operating line during hours when no public service is running. Following the satisfactory outcome of the engineers' tests, the driving instructors are allowed to drive the car for mileage accumulation trips (i.e. running without passengers). During this phase any shortcomings will be reported back to the engineers, and the driving instructor team will prepare instructional material for use in driver familiarisation courses, and compile an operating manual for the tram. (See appendix 3 for more details.) Only at the end of this process are volunteers allowed to ride on the car and provide the additional weight for testing the car's suspension! They will also stage a trial evacuation of the tramcar that will be timed.

These four photographs are by M.J. Henderson.

Glasgow 1282 (and its trucks in the foreground of this 1978 photo) set new standards in the quality of workmanship achieved in the then modestly equipped engineering facility at Crich. Sadly, this car now needs a new overhaul. Note the spare bow-collectors, hanging up ready for use.

The same car undergoing restoration at Crich in 1978.

Restoration completed, 1282 makes its first trip out of the workshop during the winter of 1978/9. Weeks of test running and mileage accumulation running would follow.

CHAPTER 9

Shunting and Abnormal Movements

9.1 The Responsibilities of Supervisory Staff and Managers.

N.B. In this section "staff" is deemed to include both employees and volunteers.

Supervisory Staff must ensure that the following Standards are met:

a Only those staff aged 16 years or above, who have been trained, passed as competent and duly authorised are allowed to couple and uncouple vehicles.

b Only those staff qualified in shunting procedures and authorised by either Duty Engineer, Outside Works Supervisor, or the Permanent Way Superintendent, can carry out the duties described in this document.

c All staff involved in shunting are in possession of requisite safety and signalling equipment.

d Any movement on the tramway system during the times when passenger services are being operated, has been authorised by the Dispatcher or Supervising Officer.

9. 2 Names and Terminology Defined

a "Shunting" is used here to describe any movement involving a railed vehicle being pulled (towed), or pushed (propelled), by another vehicle.

b The "Shunting Controller" is the co-ordinator of the activities involved in the shunting operations. This person must give clear orders/instructions to the driver of the locomotive or power unit; and to other staff involved in the shunting activities. N.B. Only the Shunting Controller may give the starting signal, whereas anyone may give a stop signal.

c "Shunter" is used in this list of procedures to describe any suitably qualified person assisting in the shunting activity.

d "Look-out" is used here to denote additional members of staff who may be deployed, as is demanded by the prevailing conditions, to promote and enhance adequate levels of safety; e.g. by guarding blind corners and watching for straying visitors, and others unaware of the moving vehicles.

e "Loco" is used here to describe any form of traction unit, i.e. tram, loco. non-railed tractor. N.B. Only those tramcars designated as suitable for towing may be used for this activity. Seek advice from the Duty Engineer before using any tram for shunting duties.

f "Abnormal Movement" means an exceptional, or irregular form of movement of a vehicle which deviates from the norm (e.g. driving from a tram's rear platform after the failure of the front-end controller).

9.3 Safety Awareness

a A positive concern regarding safety is an essential attitude of mind for all concerned. Alertness and awareness are also qualities demanded in those who are to be involved with shunting tasks. No person with hearing difficulties or impaired vision should be involved in shunting activities.

b Shunters must ensure that they are in possession of the following items of equipment before commencing their duties:

    whistle,
    suitable footwear and clothing, (i.e. of personal issue).
    wheel-chock* (if any vehicle is not fitted with a hand-brake),

and, if carrying out activities outside the depot yard:

    Red signalling flag, and
    high-visibility vests,

at night, or at times of limited visibility:

    two battery lamps.

(*Note: These chocks must only be those provided by the workshop, made of timber with a handle. Never use stones or pieces of wood for this purpose.)

c The Shunting Controller must examine before use any equipment, vehicle, track and overhead which may be used or affected by the planned movement, and report to the appropriate officer if defects or problems are evident.

d Tramcars not listed as being serviceable should only be moved after authorisation from the duty engineer.

e Before any movement is attempted, shunters should first of all think through and plan the details of the planned operation to identify and assess any potential risks and hazards. With such foresight and care accidents can be prevented.

f The Shunting Controller must brief the "shunting team" before any movement commences. The briefing must include details of all the proposed movements and highlight potential hazards. Any shunting inside the workshop building must be subject to the permission of the Duty Engineer.

g Appropriate measures must be taken to alert everyone in the vicinity of the move – explaining to visitors and anyone working near the tracks, the extent of the planned movement(s), and warning them of any possible implications to their safety. N.B. In extreme cases, a written method statement should be prepared together with a written risk assessment. Shunting activities inevitably take place in a high-risk environment (e.g. in workshops, depot-yard, or depot buildings) with visitors wandering around. Staff may be working, possibly unaware of tramcar movements – especially if shielded by doors or walls. Shunters must warn everyone in the vicinity, staff and visitors alike. Risk of malfunctions are greater when unserviceable rolling stock is being moved. Shunters must identify any hazards before moving.

9.4 General Conduct

a See and Be Seen! If in doubt, STOP. Only commence the shunting movement if visual contact is adequate between the Shunting Controller and the driver of the traction unit (e.g. loco) as well as with other persons actively involved in the shunting process.

b Listen! Always listen for a response after shouting any warning call, or giving verbal instruction. Always check that you have heard correctly, and ask for a repeat, if unsure of the instruction. Treat any indistinct call as a STOP signal.

c Hand Signals – these must be clear and distinct:
TO STOP (a) a routine stop – extended arm with the palm outstretched, or arm extended at right-angles from body (c.f. police hand signals)
TO STOP (b) in an emergency – a violent waving of the arm or arms.
TO SLOW DOWN – arm held at right angle with the palm of the hand facing down waving gently.
TO PROCEED – a clear beckoning gesture given facing the driver, except that when visibility is poor, this command is to be given by whistle. The driver should always acknowledge the starting signal by sounding the gong or horn.
CONTINUE TO PROPEL – A slow circular movement of the hand and lower arm.

d Signalling by whistle – One blast = stop, Two blasts = proceed, MULTIPLE BLASTS = emergency stop.

e Do not walk in front of moving vehicles, walk at the side of the track, close, but not too close, to the front of the leading vehicle being propelled.

f Never risk serious injury, do not run, avoid tripping up over ballast or sleeper ends. Take great care when cobbles or setts are slippery, and stay well clear of all moving wheels.

9.5 Coupling Up

a Do not touch any part of any moving vehicle, and never stand in the closing gap between vehicles while any vehicle is being moved.

b Ensure that any towbar being used is adequate and is suitable for the purpose intended (e.g. a long bar will often be required when traversing sharp curves).

c Before attempting to fix a coupling connection first make sure that both vehicles are fully braked, or wheel chocks are in place to prevent movement.

d Always place the towbar in the coupling socket of the vehicle to be towed, and then stand well clear while the loco is brought slowly forward to stand in a position where the coupling can be attached to the loco or tractor unit. Give indications to the driver of this unit of the distance required to position the coupling, but stand well clear before any movement takes place.

e Never allow your body to become an electrical "bridge" between the loco and the vehicle being coupled to it. Avoid electrocution – never ever hold the towbar in one hand and allow your other hand to touch any part of the tractor unit (i.e. tram or loco).

f Do not throw point-irons or towbars. Be safe, lift and place these items with care.

g When the coupling operation is deemed ready, the Shunting Controller must check the complete train. The current collector of the vehicle being towed must be located in a safe position. Then all chocks should be removed, the hand-brake of the vehicle being towed is to be released. Verbal warning of the impending movement (e.g. movement on track 9!) should be shouted, but remain alert for any response, then the Shunting Controller may give the "Safe to proceed" order to the driver. Everyone must remain alert for any warning shouts.

9.6 On The Move

a Never jump on or off any moving vehicle.

b Never ride in permanent-way or engineering trailers not fitted with personnel riding platforms.

c Do not travel on the entrance steps of any loco or tramcar.

d Do not lean out of cab doors, or the windows of any vehicle, while it is moving.

e Always ensure that any load being carried is properly secured.

f Ensure that all movable equipment is properly stowed at all times when moving. Do not move the crane without first anchoring the jib, unless it is carrying a load under close supervision.

g When towing or propelling vehicles fitted with brakes a shunter should be stationed to apply these brakes when signalled so to do.

h Wherever it is impossible to maintain the visual line-of-sight communication between the Shunting Controller and the loco driver, an additional member of staff must be deployed to relay signals. This can often be necessary on curved track and/or when entering buildings with relatively poor internal lighting and conditions of bright sunlight outdoors.

i The Shunting Controller is responsible for ensuring the safety of all concerned in the shunting operation, which he/she alone co-ordinates. Drivers are to follow the directions given by the Shunting Controller – unless these are in breach of the operating rules.

j The Shunting Controller should keep a watchful eye on points and frogs. Often these features cannot be seen by the driver of the loco while a vehicle is being propelled.

9.7 Drivers Involved in Shunting

a These written procedures do not replace existing instructions detailed in the Bye-Laws. Drivers are reminded that they must comply with the relevant requirements, e.g. rules for towing on gradients.

b Drivers are reminded that the Shunting Controller is in charge of the shunting operation. Drivers must not shunt on their own, even when uncomplicated movements are concerned two members of staff must be involved.

c Always keep speeds low when shunting, both while propelling and towing. Remember to be vigilant about the position of the trolley on loco and towed tramcar.

d Towing and propelling movements must be brought to a complete STOP before entering any building.

e Shunters and the driver should keep within sight of one another wherever possible. The loco driver must stop immediately if at any time visual contact with the Shunting Controller is lost.

f When moving vehicles in confined spaces, always stop short of the intended positions, and then inch forward following the directions of the shunter responsible for watching the closing gap.

g If driving from the "wrong end" the person operating the power controller must be a qualified driver. The person taking charge of the brake at the leading end must be a qualified shunter.

continued at foot of page 62

APPENDIX 1

Fault Diagnosis – No Traction

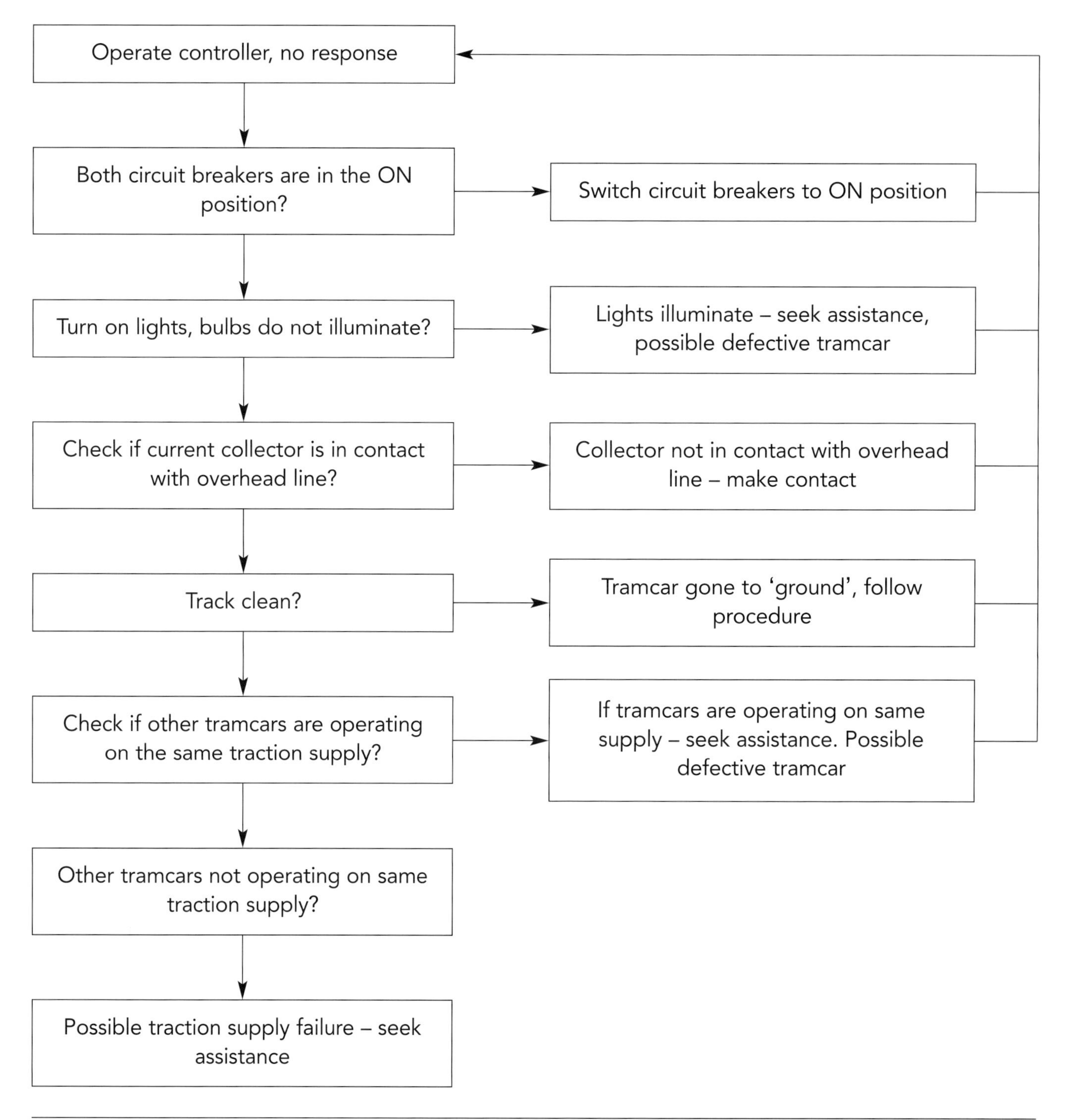

continued from page 61

9. 8 Uncoupling and Finishing the Job

a Before releasing the coupling, always ensure that the brakes have been applied to the trailer vehicle, or, if necessary, chocks are placed under the wheels.

b Apply the same level of caution described in section 9.5 for the uncoupling actions. Never park-up vehicles without first uncoupling them.

a Do not leave a tow-bar hanging from a coupling. This could present a serious trip-hazard.

d Vehicles must not be left unsupervised or unattended, except in designated safe locations.

e Unserviceable rolling stock should be left with proper warning boards when parked in the running-shed.

f Replace all moveable equipment in its correct stowage/storage place.

g Record the mileage of the shunting activity where applicable.

APPENDIX 2

Fault Diagnosis – Compressed Air System

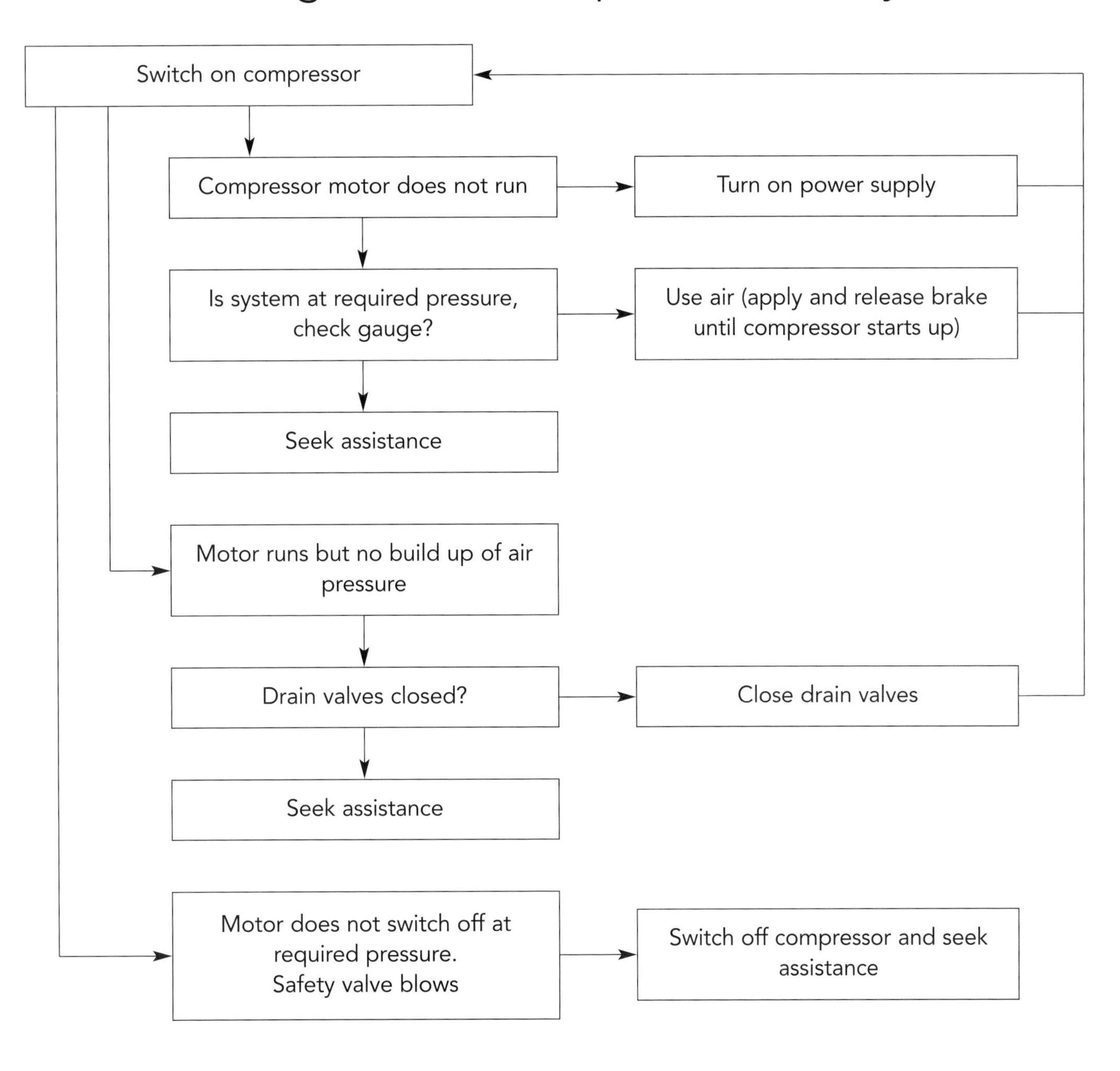

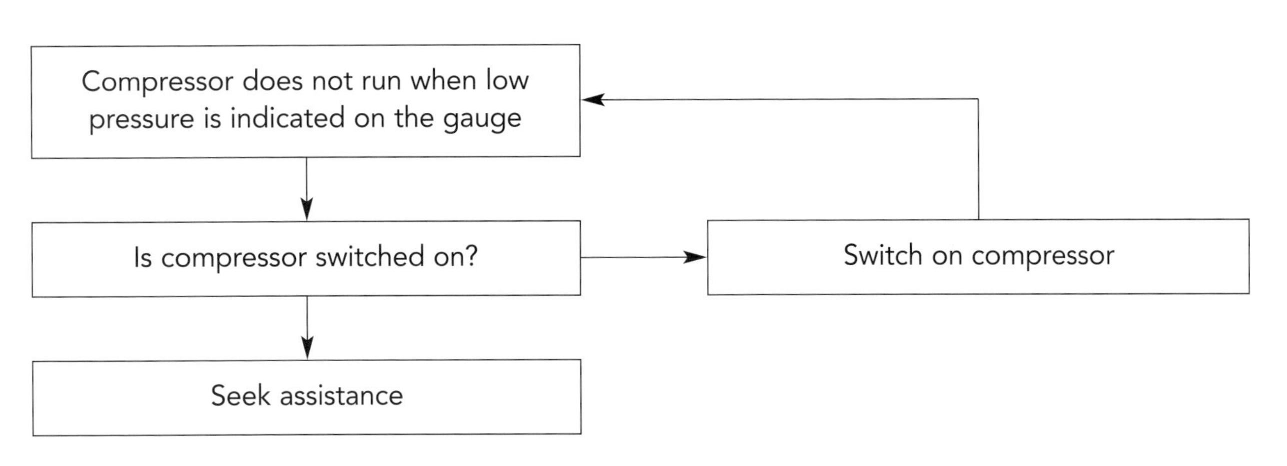

APPENDIX 3

How to write a Tramcar Operating Manual

The production of an Operating Manual for each tramcar provides an essential tool for drivers, and is best carried out as a joint effort between driving instructors and engineering staff. The Manual should provide all the information necessary for a specific tram to be operated safely and be visibly up-to-date (i.e. authorised by signature and dated), providing access to information for both drivers and conductors. Whilst the information for drivers is mostly safety critical, conductors can find a wealth of information enabling them to answer visitors' questions, and properly present the tram. A high degree of authenticity is desirable (e.g. destination and route number accurate, and in keeping with the livery and restored condition of the tram). Visitors really do appreciate seeing "their" route displayed in an authentic way.

The cover of the Manual should state the name and number of the tram, and boldly state its car classification regarding driving qualification. At Crich I introduced a colour code for the various classes making it easier for crews to locate the required manual by the colour of its cover. The introduction to the book reminds staff of the need to conserve the exhibits, and to comply fully with the standards outlined by the Museums, Archives and Libraries Council.

Here is a typical list of contents:

A START-OF-DAY CHECKS
B LIMITATIONS
C LAY-OUT OF EQUIPMENT
D OPERATING THE TRAM
E TECHNICAL DESCRIPTION AND HISTORY OF THE CAR
F PROBLEM SOLVING

The start-of-day checks provides a reminder of what to check and where to locate the equipment that needs checking. Some items are well concealed under seats, and in cupboards.

Limitations is divided into two parts: The Do's and the Don'ts. It provides a series of bullet-points highlighting what you can do and what you must not do, with the tram, e.g. whether or not the tram can access all the depot tracks. This particular section can swiftly be read by a relief driver who has to take over the tram for a lunch-time meal break relief, and needs to be able to refresh his/her memory of the car's special features in a matter of minutes.

The layout of equipment section informs the driver where to locate items of portable equipment, and the location of switches and details their function. Blackpool Tramways for example fitted no fewer than three change-over switches in the lighting circuits. One at each end changes over the head and tail-light at the adjacent dash panel. The third switch transfers the platform light from one platform to the other.

Operating the tram provides an insight into the performance of the tram and its shortcomings. Again, the class of tram known as "Blackpool Standards" provides a ready example. This design was suited to the flat streets of the resort. Only two axles (out of four) are motored, and consequently the performance on hills is less than impressive. Even worse is the less than sure-footed adhesion between wheels and rail. Only fifty percent of the car's weight is on the two driving axles, so under poor rail conditions the driver's skills will be tested.

Section E is self-explanatory. It should not only provide a short summary of engineering features, but also a brief summary of modifications (if any) that were made to the car during its working career. The potted history is designed to refresh tram-crews' knowledge of the tram and so equip them with accurate information to give to passengers during the brief talk provided during waiting time.

Information regarding destination blinds should be two-fold: a complete list of destinations carried by the blinds (sometimes when all the blinds are different, a list for each individual blind is required). It can be very frustrating to wind through an entire destination blind and discover that the sought after place-name is not carried. A second list in the manual will provide a route description, matching destinations with appropriate route numbers and/or "via" blinds (if fitted).

The final section provides hints for use in elementary fault finding. Last, but not least, there is a page for staff to list suggestions for improvement or additions to the manual. This can provide a valuable resource and makes the manuals seem less the work of the "experts", and more of a collective enterprise.

The format of the manuals is A5 paper-back. Previously, an elaborate page lettering/numbering system had been used for the revision and replacement of individual pages. With modern word-processing systems an electronic master copy can be updated within seconds and a new print off can be quickly produced. A replacement copy for the more popular trams' manuals is necessary (even without amendments) on an annual basis.

A typical short history of tram Newcastle 102 of the National Tramway Museum collection:

The tram was delivered from Hurst Nelson's Motherwell factory in 1901. It was one of a batch of thirty single-deck open-sided tramcars. Perhaps the Edwardians were expecting climate change, but it soon became obvious that summers in the North-East are seldom warm or prolonged. Within a couple of years the complete class was put through the corporation's tram works at Byker; the resulting design (open-topped double-decker) being more suitable for all year round operation.

Tramcar 102 was originally equipped with B.T.H. B3 controllers and four traction-motors. Modifications were made to the tram in 1936 when deeper decency panels were mounted along the top deck, and air-brakes were fitted in an attempt to improve the braking effectiveness of this heavy type of car.

Unsuitable for the hillier routes on the Newcastle system, the car's main employment was from Byker depot on the Scotswood Road and Gosforth routes. Sunday duties saw this class of car used on the Gosforth Park circular, and at other times it saw service on race-day specials.

Withdrawn from service in February 1949, car 102 was presented by Newcastle Corporation to the Museum Committee of the then Light Railway Transport League for preservation, and left Byker depot by lorry in April 1950. This development was at the beginning of tramcar preservation by amateurs in this country. These pioneers later became the founding members of the Tramway Museum Society at its formation in 1955.

Tram 102 was the largest tramcar of the then collection and the problems of housing a tram of this size meant that it was subjected to many moves, being transported around the country in search of permanent storage facilities during the years before 1975 when at last it arrived at Crich.

Car 102 first spent time in storage at Benton (Newcastle). In 1954 it was moved to a bus garage in Bury (Lancs). This was followed by a period of outdoor display at Beaulieu (Hants). Then it was transported back to Byker Depot (Newcastle), where restoration work to remedy the decaying bodywork commenced in 1967. Three years later the car was moved to Clay Cross store before making a triumphant return to passenger service at Crich on 21 July 1975.

A brief visit to Newcastle to mark the opening of the Metro light rail system in November 1981 was followed some years later by a longer sojourn in Gateshead during the Summer of 1990, when car 102 operated on the specially built National Garden Festival tramway. Even though it has been out of service for some years now, by the year 2006 it will have clocked up fifty-six years in preservation – truly quite an achievement.

Part of the high-speed Middleton Light Railway of Leeds City Tramways, at Parkside. The motorway has obliterated this location completely.

Leeds was my favourite first generation tramway, and although my grandmother lived near Sheffield the highlight of any holiday with her was a trip by bus to Leeds. Service speeds of the trams were much higher there than in the other Yorkshire city, and the fleet had many exotic varieties of tram. Here are some of my cherished photos from May 1958.

Feltham car at Halton terminus. As the tram on which I rode from Temple Newsham got level with the Feltham and stopped, a heated argument arose between the two drivers about which tram was scheduled to leave first (and collect the most passengers on its way back to the city!).

Belle Isle terminus showing the two types of tram which survived until the end of tramway operation Leeds in November 1959.

BIBLIOGRAPHY

English Language

This is a selection – most tramway operators produced their own Rules and Regulations; other articles on the subject can be found in transport periodicals and in-house magazines.

Air Brake Apparatus for Electric Tramways and Light Railways, The Consolidated Brake and Engineering Co. Ltd., January 1929

Belfast City Tramways, Rules and Regulations for Motormen & Conductors 1908

Birmingham and Midland Tramways Joint Committee, Rules and Regulations 1926

Birmingham Corporation Rules & Regulations, 1926 & 1937

Bolton Corporation Rules & Regulations 1901

Brakes for Tramway Cars
H.M.Sayers
The Electrician Printing and Publishing Co. 1907

Bristol Tramways Co. Rules and Regulations, 1900, reprinted 1990

British Railways Track Design Construction and Maintenance
Second reprint 1950
Edited by R.A.Hamnett
The Permanent Way Institution
Sixth edition 1993
Edited by G.Cope
ISBN 0 903489 03 1

British Tramway Accidents
F.E.Wilson, edited by G.Claydon
2006, Adam Gordon
ISBN 1 874422 58 3

(The) Bus and Coach Driving Manual,
Driving Standards Agency
HMSO, 1997
ISBN 0 11 551784 7

Cork Electric Tramways & Lighting Co. Rules and Regulations 1898

Developing and maintaining staff competence
Railway Safety Principles and Guidance, Part 3, Section A
Health and Safety Executive
HM Railway Inspectorate, 2002
ISBN 0 717617 32 7

Edinburgh Street Tramways Co, Rules and Regulations for the Servants, 1883
Reprinted 1995 by Adam Gordon
ISBN 1 874422 13 3

Electric Power and Traction
F.H.Davies
Archibald Constable & Co. 1907

Electric Railways and Tramways – their Construction and Operation
P.Dawson
Engineering, 1897

Electrical Traction, F.Lydall & E.Wilson
Edward Arnold, volumes 1 & 2, 1907

Electric Railways, Theoretically and Practically Treated
S.W.Ashe & J.D.Keiley, 1905
A.Constable & Co. Ltd.

Electric Traction
R.H.Smith
Harper & Brothers, 1905

Electric Traction
A.T.Dover
First edition 1917, Whitaker & Co.
Second impression, corrected 1919
Sir Isaac Pitman & Sons
Fourth impression, corrected 1915
Second edition 1929
Second edition reprinted 1937
Third edition 1954
Fourth edition 1963
Fourth edition reprinted 1965

Electric Traction, J.H.Rider
Whittaker & Co. 1903

Electric Traction E.Wilson
Edward Arnold, 1897

Electric Traction Handbook
R.Brooks, 1953
Sir Isaac Pitman & Sons

Electricity in Transport
The English Electric Co. Ltd. 1951

International Correspondence School Library -
Tramway Systems, Tracks, Overhead Work & Cars and Equipment, Brakes and Brake Rigging, Tramway Motors and Controllers
Direct-Current Railways and Alternating Current on Railways, Electric Signalling on Railways, 1914, 1920 & 1921

Electric Street Railways
E.J.Houston and A.E.Kennelly, 1896

Electric Tramcar Handbook, W.A.Agnew, various editions from 1904 (1st), H.Alabaster Gatehouse & Co. to 1920 (8th), The Electrical Review Ltd.

The "Engineering" and Electric Traction Pocket-Book
P.Dawson, 1903

Gateshead and District Tramways Co. – Rules and Regulations, 1901

Glasgow Corporation Transport, Tramway Section, Rules and Regulations, 1935 & 1950

A History of the British Steam Tram
D.G.Gladwin, volume 1, 2004
Adam Gordon
ISBN 1 874422 46 X

Ditto, volume 2, 2006
ISBN 1 874422 56 7

How to Become a Competent Motorman
V.B.Livermore & J.Williams, 1902
Brooklyn Rapid Transit Co.

Jarrow & District Electric Traction Co.
Rules & Regulations applying to Motormen and Conductors, 1917

Kidderminster & Stourport Electric Tramway Co. Rules & Regulations for Officers and Servants, 1899
Reprinted 1991 by Adam Gordon
ISBN 1 874422 01 X

Larger and Working Objects
A guide to their preservation and care
S.Bell, edited by P.Winsor
Museums and Galleries Commission
First published in 1997, ISBN 0 948630 52 1

London County Council Tramways – Pullman Review, 1932

London County Council Tramways, Rules and Regulations for Motormen, n.d

London County Council Tramways, Motorman's Handbook, 1928, reprinted in 1995 by Adam Gordon, Parchment (Oxford) Ltd.
ISBN 1 874422 14 1

London Transport, Rule Book for Drivers and Conductors, 1944, reprinted 1951

Manchester Corporation Tramways Instructions for Drivers & Guards
1914 edition reprinted 1970 by Manchester Transport Museum Society, 1927

Manx Electric Railway, Rules and Regulations
Reprint of 1926 edition

Metropolitan Electric & London United Tramways Ltd, South Metropolitan Electric Tramways & Lighting Co. Ltd.
Conditions of Service, Rules, Regulations and Instructions for Motormen and Conductors 1928

My 50 Years in Transport
A.G.Grundy
Tramway & Railway World Publishing Co. 1944, reprinted by Adam Gordon, 1997,
ISBN 1 874422 19 2

Next Stop Seaton – 50 Years of Modern Electrsic Tramways Ltd.
D.Jay and D.Voice
Adam Gordon, 2003
ISBN 1 874422 43 5

Outlines of Electrical Engineering
H.H.Simmonds
Cassell & Co. 1909

Principles of Direct Current Electric Traction, D.W.Hinde & H.E.Ingham
George Newnes Ltd. 1946

The Railway Dictionary
A.A.Jackson,
Third edition 2000
Sutton Publishing Ltd.
ISBN 0 750925 54 X

Railway Safety Principles and Guidance
Part 2 section G, Guidance on tramways
Health & Safety Executive
HM Railway Inspectorate
First published July 1997
Revised and web version 2005

Railway safety critical work
Railways (Safety Critical Work) Regulations 1994
Approved Code of Practice & Guidance
Health & Safety Commission
Section edition 1996, ISBN 0 717612 60 0

Tramways of Reading
H.E.Jordan
Reprint of 1957 original by Adam Gordon, 1990
ISBN 1 874422 00 1

Rotherham Corporation Tramways, Rules & Regulations 1904

Salford City Transport, Regulations and Instructions for Motormen, Conductors and Trolley Boys, n.d.

Salford Corporation Transport – Regulations and Instructions for Drivers, Conductors and Youths 1945

Sheffield Corporation Tramways – Motormen and Conductors, Rules & Regulations, 1926

A Source Book of Trams
J.H.Price
Ward Lock & Co., 1980
ISBN 0 706360 57 5

Standards in the Museum Care of Large and Working Objects
Social and Industrial History Collections 1994
Museums & Galleries Commission
ISBN 0 948630 26 4

Stockport Corporation Rules and Regulations for Drivers and guards, 1928

Street Railways, Their Construction, Operation and Maintenance
C.B.Fairchild, 1892
Reprinted 2005 by Adam Gordon
ISBN 1 874422

Through the Cities
M.Barry
Frankfort Press, 1991
ISBN 0 95106 9 63 2

Training of Drivers and Conductors of Buses, Trams and Trolleybuses
London Transport, Curwen Press 1936
Reprinted by Adam Gordon 1995
ISBN 1 874422 15 X

Tramway Motorman's Handbook
W.S.Ibbetson
E. & F. N.Spon, 1920

Tramways – their Construction and Working
D.Kinnear Clark
Volume 1 1878, volume 2 1882
Crosby Lockwood & Co.
Second edition 1894
Reprinted 1992, and 2006 by Adam Gordon
ISBNs 1 874422 04 4 & 1 874422 59 1

The Wheels Used to Talk to Us
T.Cooper ed.
Tallis Publishing, first edition 1977
ISBN 0 950545 80 5
Reprinted by Sheaf Publishing 1977 & 1980

Tramways and Electric Railways in the 19th Century
Cassiers Electric Railway Number 1899
ISBN 1 874422 03 6
Reprinted in 1960 by the Light Railway Transport League, and by Adam Gordon in 1992

The Wearing of the Green – reminiscences of the Glasgow Trams
W.M.Tollan
2000, Adam Gordon
ISBN 1 874422 27 3

German Language

BO Strab [Regulations for construction and operation of Tramways]
Verband Deutscher Verkehrs Unternehmen, Cologne
Edition of 2000

Chronik der Strassenbahn
P.H. Prasuhn
Published by M & H Schaper, Verlag, Hannover 1969

Dienstanweisung für den Fahrdienst der Strassenbahn (DF Strab).
Fachgruppe Strassenbahn 1942, reprinted 1983.

Dienstanweisung für den Fahrdienst mit Strassenbahnen (DF Strab).
Verband Deutscher Verkehrs Unternehmen, Cologne 1989
(DF Strab is the abbreviation for Tramway Rule Book.)

Handbuch der Deutschen Strassenbahngeschichte, by Wolfgang Hendlmeier
Munich 1979. (Doctoral Thesis, Two Volumes, short English Summary)

Handbuch Strassenbahn Fahrzeuge, Anlage, Betriebe
Ivo Köhler, Published by Geramond Verlag, Munich, 2006
ISBN 3-7654-7142-9

Stadtbahnen in Deutschland – Light Rail in Germany
Produced by the Federal Ministry of Transport, and the V.D.V., Alba Publishing, Düsseldorf 2000.
(Definitive work, parallel text in German and English.)

Strassenbahn Archiv DDR, Vols 1-7
Editor Dr-Ing. Gerhard Bauer,
Verlag Ingrid Zeunert, Berlin (East) 1981
This series is now being reprinted (in 2006) by publisher: Transpress of Stuttgart.

Strassenbahnfibel, Stuttgart, 1949
Reprinted by the Stuttgart Tramway Museum in 1980

Der Strassenbahn Fahrmeister
Fritz Lehner
Published by Felix Meiner Verlag
Leipzig, 1948

Der Strassenbahner
Published by Verband Deutscher Verkehrs Unternehmen
Cologne 2001

INDEX

...The End

The end of the driving school in March 1968 was marked with a group photo (as well as a party where the penalty "fines" for trainees missing any section insulators were converted into beer!).

The end of the line at Eanam terminus in Blackburn. Buffer stops made from old tram rail were a feature of the town's tramway. The drawing below from 1901 may indicate the reason for such end-of-line protection. The steam tram trailer almost dragged the loco into the river with it! *Photographer Unknown*

From the *Blackburn Weekly Telegraph* of 13 April 1901.

The end of the training course at Crich in 1989 for the technicians who were due to maintain the trams at the Gateshead Garden Festival, was also commemorated with a group photo in front of newly restored Sunderland 100 (now preserved as M.E.T 331). Sadly, our coach-painter's work was all in vain, as the car's sponsors insisted that their own corporate livery was applied.

The end is nigh for this Liverpool Baby Grand, a four-wheel economy version of the Green Goddess design, as it awaits the wreckers in the sidings at Edge Lane works. In the background can be seen a similar car passing by on the main road. Car 245 of this class is awaiting restoration in Birkenhead.

OTHER SELECTED TRANSPORT BOOKS

BY

ADAM GORDON

KINTRADWELL FARMHOUSE, BRORA, SUTHERLAND KW9 6LU
Tel: 01408 622660
e-mail: adam@ahg-books.com

The Life of Isambard Kingdom Brunel, by his son, reprint of the 1870 edition, s/b, 604pp, £20
The Cable System of Tramway Traction, reprint of 1896 publication, 56pp, s/b, £10
The Definitive Guide to Trams (including Funiculars) in the British Isles, 3rd edition; D. Voice, s/b, A5, 248pp, £20
Double-Deck Trams of the World, Beyond the British Isles, B. Patton, A4 s/b, 180pp, £18
Double-Deck Trolleybuses of the World, Beyond the British Isles; B. Patton, A4, s/b, 96pp, £16
Edinburgh's Transport, vol. 2, 1919-1975, D. Hunter, 192pp, s/b, £20
The Feltham Car of the Metropolitan Electric and London United Tramways, reprint of 1931 publication, s/b, 18pp, £5
Glasgow Subway Album, G. Watson, A4 s/b, all colour, 64pp, £10
How to Go Tram and Tramway Modelling, third edition, D. Voice, B4, 152pp, completely rewritten, s/b, £20
My 50 Years in Transport, A.G. Grundy, 54 pp, s/b, 1997, £10
Omnibuses & Cabs, Their Origin and History, H.C. Moore, h/b reprint with d/w, 282pp, £25
The Overhaul of Tramcars, reprint of LT publication of 1935, 26pp, s/b, £6
Next Stop Seaton! – Golden Jubilee history of Modern Electric Tramways Ltd., David Jay & David Voice, B5 softback, 136pp, covers coloured on both sides, £17
The History of the Steam Tram, H. Whitcombe, h/b, over 60pp, £12
A History of the British Steam Tram, volume 1, David Gladwin, case bound, coloured covers, 176pp, 312 x 237mm, profusely illustrated, £40
A History of the British Steam Tram, volume 2, D. Gladwin, hardback, 256pp, £40
The History and Development of Steam Locomotion on Common Roads, W. Fletcher, reprint of 1891 edition, 332pp, £18
Street Railways, their construction, operation and maintenance, by C.B. Fairchild, reprint of 1892 publication, 496pp, hardback, profusely illustrated, £40
Toy and Model Trams of the World – Volume 1: Toys, die casts and souvenirs; Gottfried Kuøe and David Voice, A4 s/b, all colour, 128pp, £25
Toy and Model Trams of the World – Volume 2: Plastic, white metal and brass models and kits. Gottfried Kuøe and David Voice, A4 s/b all colour, 188pp, £30
My Life in Many States and in Foreign Lands, G.F. Train, reprint of his autobiography, over 350pp, s/b, £12
Trams, Trolleybuses and Buses and the Law before De-regulation, M. Yelton, B4, s/b, 108pp, £15
Tramways – Their Construction & Working, D. Kinnear Clark, reprint of the 1894 edition, softback, 812pp. £28
Life of Richard Trevithick, two volumes in one, reprint of 1872 edition, softback, 830pp, £25
The Twilight Years of the trams in Aberdeen & Dundee; all colour, A4 s/b, introduction and captions by A. Brotchie, 120pp, £25
The Twilight Years of the Edinburgh Tram, 112pp, A4 s/b, includes 152 coloured pics, £25
The Twilight Years of the Glasgow Tram, over 250 coloured views, A4, s/b, 144 pp, £25
The Wantage Tramway, S.H. Pearce Higgins, with Introduction by John Betjeman, h/b reprint with d/w, over 158pp, £28
The Wearing of the Green, being reminiscences of the Glasgow trams, W. Tollan, s/b, 96pp, £12

TERMS

RETAIL UK – for post and packing please add 10% of the value of the order up to £4.90 maximum, apart from the Brunel biography and Street Railways, which because of their weight, please add £3, and £5 respectively. Orders £50 and over post and packing free. I regret that I am not yet equipped to deal with credit/debit cards.
RETAIL OVERSEAS – postage will be charged at printed paper rate via surface mail, unless otherwise requested. Payment please by sterling cash or cheque, UK sterling postage stamps, or direct bank to bank by arrangement.
SOCIETIES, CHARITIES, etc. relating to tramways, buses and railways – a special 50% discount for any quantity of purchases is given **provided my postal charges are paid**.
WHOLESALE (TRADE) DISCOUNTS FOR MULTIPLE COPIES OF THE SAME TITLE, UK post free:
1-15 copies – 35%; 16-30 copies – 40%; 31-45 copies – 45%; 46 & over – 50%